'ALLO 'ALLO!

THE WAR DIARIES OF RENÉ ARTOIS

VOLUME 2

THE EXPLOSIVE BESTSELLER!

Based on the
BBC Television series by
Jeremy Lloyd and
David Croft

Edited and with an
introduction by
René Fairfax

Translated by
John Haselden

BBC BOOKS

My fondest wishes
to Roger*

Published by BBC Books,
a division of BBC Enterprises Limited
Woodlands, 80 Wood Lane, London W12 0TT
First published 1989
Reprinted 1989

'Allo 'Allo! television scripts © David Croft and
Jeremy Lloyd, 1984, 1986, 1987, 1988, 1989
This book © John Haselden 1989
ISBN 0 563 20842 2

Cover and page design concept:
Hammond Hammond
Art director: Roger Hammond
Illustrations: Jean Hurd, Toula Antonakos, Larry Rostant,
Oonah O'toole, Robert Gage

All photographs are BBC © except for the following:
page 22 (background) PLANET NEWS,
pages 29, 64, 90 (backgrounds) HULTON PICTURE COMPANY

Set in 11 on 13 point Century Bold
Printed and bound in Great Britain by
Butler & Tanner Ltd, Frome, Somerset
Cover printed by Belmont Press Ltd,
Northampton

*René's dedication page was unfortunately severely damaged, but I feel sure this is the message he intended.

ACKNOWLEDGEMENTS

In keeping with René's fondness for the performing arts, I have decorated the text with excerpts from poetry and songs commissioned for the café, from old favourites like 'It's the Wrong Way to Tickle René' to the more contemporary sound of 'Two Little Bols' and the ever-popular 'Cheese Release Me'.

The Nouvion Transport Museum has kindly permitted the reproduction of their priceless collection of Crabtree's parking tickets.

Hubert Gruber has donated many duplicate photographs of himself. He gave all the originals to the bravest café-owner in all France at one time or another, but says they were virtually all mysteriously destroyed.

General Von Klinkerhoffen, Helga, Herr Flick and Colonel Von Strohm are all seen from some interesting new angles in the never-before-published highlights from Englebert Von Smallhausen's secret correspondence with his mother.

As always, I have relied on the enormous support of my editor, Sheila Ableman, and am indebted to John Haselden, my translator, for communicating once more a sense of the nuances and subtleties of the great man's prose.

And last, but certainly not least, there is a limited-edition full-colour forgery of the Fallen Madonna with the Big Boobies sewn into the centre pages of the first 500,000 copies printed of this book. Your number is 500,001.

500,001

INTRODUCTION

The successful publication of the first volume of *The War Diaries of René Artois* has unleashed an appetite amongst readers of discrimination which must be satisfied.

I myself confess to having become considerably excited by the great man's revelations and, though I began by thinking that they would only afford me a light though tasty literary snack, I have now realised that we can make a meal of them.

Volume One, of course, was all over by Christmas 1941, but Yvette Carte Blanche, my mother, had often referred tantalisingly to René's many other entries. Thus I made it my business to unearth evidence of further memoirs. The search took me very far afield. From the bordellos of Trastèvre to the Auction Rooms of Buenos Aires I exerted myself tirelessly. Nonetheless, I still managed to find the energy to get to grips with a mature Christmas pudding that had been served to Yvette recently in the buffet car on the train from Nouvion to Paris. Recognising it immediately, she had brought it home concealed about her person. She assured me it contained something very explosive.

She was right. I prodded it gently with a fork. There was a big bang, and the pudding was blown all over the kitchen, along with several thousand words of the second volume of *The War Diaries of René Artois*. Sharp-sighted readers will realise this explains certain unfortunate gaps in the text which follows.

There is still cause for celebration, however. I was able to piece the manuscript painstakingly together, and found that I had much important archive material on my hands, not to mention my face and neck.

Despite Edith's best efforts, it is René's voice which once again unmistakably colours the text, along with a great many scorch-marks and morsels of pudding. But it is typical of the man's generosity that he very rarely stands alone. Many of the protagonists in this drama are given the chance to reveal themselves, and often in a startling light.

We continue to gain privileged access to Colonel Von Strohm's plans for the post-war art market, to the terrible instrument of torture lurking in Herr Flick's private quarters, and to General Von Klinkerhoffen's detailed preparations for Hitler's birthday.

We see a great deal of Helga, and slightly less of Mimi Labonq and Englebert Von Smallhausen (especially after one of the Nouvion church bells falls on him).

The volume also contains much evidence of René the visionary. My mother often told me that the great man was capable of huge leaps of the imagination, and rarely is this better illustrated than by his proposal for a *Blue Guide to Nouvion*, for which he intended to take personal responsibility. He foresaw a considerable increase in traffic through the entire region between '42 and '45, and aimed

to capitalise upon it. Excerpts from the guide, with maps and cross-sections, are dotted through the text.

We find ourselves on an intimate tour through what he liked to call Artois Country, stopping at the butcher's with the big chopper, Herr Flick's dungeon, Hubert Gruber's favourite positions and much more besides. Not for nothing had he penned the slogan which was to become a byword in the Nouvion market: '1942 – Open for Business.'

Amongst the charred pages of this historic document we also discover a surprise or two waiting in the hat shop of the girl with the big berets and, closer to home, the little cupboard under the stairs. Many critics have been puzzled by the variety and extent of the entertainment available in a town of such modest proportions but, as René himself said on more than one occasion, size is not everything. Also, this was before the advent of television.

It was clear to me from the outset that the further memoirs of the greatest hero in all France contains material of an inflammatory nature. For a start, René has written much of his diary for 1942 in a code which is so complex that at first I assumed I had scraped it off the ceiling in the wrong order.

René Fairfax
Artois Country
April 1989

1 JANUARY

Perhaps it is inevitable that, despite my continued attempts to turn the tides of war in our favour, my heroism remains unsung. My wife Edith offered to put things right at the party last night with a couple of verses detailing the exact nature of my achievements, but I modestly declined.

Only Yvette really appreciates the value of my work undercover. I sent a message to her yesterday morning: Meet me in the Gruber at eight o'nibble for a position. Lieutenant pantry was clocking his favourite Bols in at the bar again, and I only just escaped a drink.*

* *There is no question in my mind about the significance of this message. Though I have still not quite cracked René's code, those of us who are lucky enough to have been privy to his exploits will deduce that Nighthawk was about to strike once more for France.*

    During the course of such entries one begins to understand something of the complex nature of René's relationship with my mother, Yvette, though where 'the Gruber' fitted in one can only speculate.

Oh heck. Things are going very badly.

Ten months ago I was shot and apparently killed by a German firing squad. I have been in terrible pain ever since. Not only did the wooden bullets Colonel Von Strohm managed to substitute for the real ones leave appalling splinters, but also I have had to watch Edith inherit the café and spend all my money.

And that is not all.

I have had to expend a great deal of precious energy supervising Yvette and my new waitress, Mimi Labonq, as they serve under me.

I have had to expend even more backing away from the advances of Lieutenant Gruber, who is still suffering from the scars left by the Russian Front and will insist on trying to show them to me. Since my execution I have had to masquerade as René, my own twin brother from Nancy, and Hubert has never made a secret of his fondness for Nancy boys. Not recently, anyway.

The long and the short of it is that I was a shadow of my former self even before I was captured by Denise Laroque, my childhood sweetheart and now the fanatical leader of the Communist Resistance, in mid-December last year. I am a man who usually has no difficulty getting his Laroques off, but I have to say I was no match for Denise. She is insatiable. There were times when I thought it would be all over by Christmas.

Having offered myself for the freedom of my marginally less courageous comrades, I had no alternative but to lie back and think of England. Or Spain, or Sweden, or Switzerland – anywhere, in fact, where I could make a tactical withdrawal and live to fight another day.

After a week I was tempted to surrender. Fortunately, I was able to negotiate a settlement. I promised that we would be married when she had a moment to spare in-between blowing up trains and bridges and things, and as soon as I could take a break from my various acts of heroism.

In the meantime I agreed that she could borrow the original canvases of the Fallen Madonna with the Big Boobies by Van Clomp and the Cracked Vase with the Big Daisies by Van Gogh which I had cunningly concealed in the headquarters of the Communist Resistance. She said she would keep the forgeries I had as well.

3 JANUARY

I returned to downtown Nouvion a broken man. Fortunately Yvette was able to massage some feeling back into my aching limbs, and I was back in my usual position at the café in time to make the most of the season of goodwill. I'm glad to say the takings at the bar over the Christmas period were quite substantial as well.

I have only just recovered sufficient strength to begin recording my exploits once more for posterity.

René makes a small adjustment to his dickie. So does Monsieur Leclerc.

1·9·4·2

OPEN FOR BUSINESS

The bravest cafe-owner in all France sees unparalleled opportunities for profit in the coming year. 'Now that Hitler has changed the rules governing market forces,' he says proudly, 'we should all take advantage of the potential for growth.'

4 JANUARY

The New Year is traditionally a time for taking stock. As
I polished the glasses at the bar this evening I ran through
mine. It didn't take much time. Thanks to my wife's
mother, we were short on gin. Thanks to Colonel Von
Strohm and Captain Bertorelli we were long on
knockwurst and salami. Thanks to Denise Laroque and
the Nouvion West Sub Area of the Communist Resistance,
we were short on canvases of the Fallen Madonna with
the Big Boobies and the Cracked Vase with the Big Daisies.

'You are very preoccupied tonight, René,' Lieutenant
Gruber said.

'You are going to have to get your lipstick and brushes
out again, Lieutenant,' I replied.

'Ah, René.' He smiled that little smile of his that I find
so unsettling. 'I have long dreamed of this moment. What
do you have in mind?'

'Another couple of forgeries of the Fallen Madonna
with the Big Boobies,' I said quickly.

5 JANUARY

My wife is still determined to marry me, despite her
mother's advice and the threats of the fanatical leader of
the Communist Resistance (Nouvion West Sub Area). As
so often in life, this has its advantages and its
disadvantages.

The disadvantages have been fairly obvious to anyone
who has heard my wife sing. The advantage is that I got
to spend an hour or so at the keyhole of the back room this
afternoon watching Madame Lenare of the Brides
Parisienne Boutique showing her some little items of
lingerie for our wedding-night. And I must say they suited
Madame Lenare very well.

For some reason, watching this exceptionally gifted
woman in action reminded me forcibly of a particular

painting by Van Clomp that I am anxious to get my hands on again. If I do not, General Von Klinkerhoffen will not get his forgery, nor will Herr Flick of the Gestapo and nor will Hitler who has already promised it to Eva for her birthday. Several times. Needless to say if they do not gain satisfaction they will each place a great deal of pressure on Colonel Von Strohm, who may in turn feel it necessary to mention my name.

It is fortunate in this instance that Lieutenant Gruber has artistic leanings. I decided to ask him if he was up to forging the Fallen Madonna with the Big Boobies from memory.

On second thoughts, I realised that this was one of my more optimistic schemes. He could have touched up the Laughing Cavalier with his eyes shut, but the Fallen Madonna required a slightly different approach.

Perhaps Madame Lenare could model for him. I checked the view through the key hole again and began to wonder whether we would ever be able to find enough paint.

6 JANUARY

Last night as we retired Edith approached me with the sort of twinkle in her eye that I am glad to say I have not encountered since the early days of our marriage.

'René,' she said, 'I have selected for our wedding-night some lovely surprises. Madame Lenare has some beautiful things under the counter.'

'She has some pretty good things above the counter,' I replied, wondering where all this would lead. I decided to take evasive action and suddenly remembered that I might have forgotten to turn the light off in the cellar.

As I descended the steps from the bar I had a brief, wistful memory of Maria before she posted herself to Switzerland in a Red Cross parcel. She used to get very dirty down there.

No sooner had the thought crossed my mind than a

pair of small but incredibly powerful arms encircled me and I felt Mimi Labonq's hot breath on the small of my back.

'Why are you trying to avoid me?' she whispered hoarsely. 'Now we are together let me do something that will make you feel warm and wonderful.'

'Good idea,' I said, attempting to shake her off. 'You can fill my hot-water bottle.'

I don't know what she does to the enemy, but she scares out of me the living daylights.

7 JANUARY

I've just found out what she does to the enemy, given half a chance.

Herr Flick of the Gestapo was entertaining Helga, the Colonel's personal secretary, in the back room tonight.

'Mimi,' I instructed, 'the menu, and wine for Herr Flick and his bit of . . . his lady.'

'I have already prepared a bottle for the Gestapo,' she growled.

I went swiftly through to check the table settings, and to make sure that the British airmen had already left by the window.

I was just closing the curtains when that idiot Crabtree appeared outside.

'Good moaning,' he said. His sense of time is only marginally better than his ability to speak our language.

'Good evening, officer. How comforting to know that you are doing your duty. Now go away and stop wasting your torch.'

'It is a dick night.'

'Very likely,' I said, my week with Denise flashing unaccountably before me.

'I thought I saw two men leaking by your dustbins.'

'Well that is France for you,' I said.

Mimi ushered Herr Flick into the room. 'Here you are, sir,' she growled. 'You will never drink a better bottle.'

Herr Flick about to knock up another Fallen Madonna.

'I will open it,' Herr Flick ordered.

'Herr Flick, when you behave in such a dominating fashion I go weak at the knees.' Helga's eyes shone.

'Only the knees?' I heard Flick reply as I left, pushing Mimi before me.

I felt it was time to give her a small lecture in the finer points of the restaurateur's art. I was tempted to give her a big lecture, but she simply wasn't the right height.

'Mimi,' I said authoritatively, 'you must not oversell our wine. We only give the Gestapo plonk, and it was very unwise telling him that he will never drink a better bottle.'

'It was the truth,' she growled. 'I removed the cork and put in the bottle a deadly poison. In four minutes he will be no more.'

'Mimi!' I cried, seeing my chances of a five-star rating in the *Michelin Guide* disappearing before my very eyes. 'Not in my café!'

I crashed through the door just as Herr Flick was giving the toast.

'May we be blessed with many little members of the Master Race...'

To his astonishment, I seized both glasses from their outstretched hands and emptied them on to the floor. The bottle I chucked out of the window.

There was a rather uneasy silence.

'It was not a good year,' I said.

20 JANUARY

For the last fortnight I have been quite unable to write. We men of action have to resign ourselves to the fact that moments of peaceful contemplation are often denied us. And what with avoiding the attentions of the Communist Resistance and attempting to prevent Mimi from wiping out a substantial proportion of my clientèle on the premises, I have been more or less perpetually on the move.

21 JANUARY

Last night I heard that Denise Laroque would still not rest until the women in my life have been rubbed out. The message was attached to a large stick of dynamite which came through the front window of the café, but fortunately extinguished itself in Lieutenant Gruber's port and lemon.

    I wondered whether the moment had finally come for me to retire to the Spanish border and regroup.

    I made a mental note of the defences that stood between me and the fanatical leader of the Communist Resistance as I poured the Lieutenant another drink.

    There was Mimi, my little handgrenade, who was small but highly explosive at close quarters.

    There was Yvette, my big bazooka, who was always prepared to deploy her weaponry on a variety of fronts.

    And there was Edith, whom I have always looked upon as the ultimate deterrent.*

    But what chance would they have if I stayed?

    'You look troubled, René,' said Lieutenant Gruber.

    'I'm just thinking about my arsenal,' I replied.

    'Me too,' he said, with that little smile of his that I find so unsettling. 'Anything I can do to help?'

* *Edith Artois never gave up singing in public, even though she was asked to on many occasions. Even at the end of her life her vocal range was quite stunning.*

CABARET 9~10pm

CAFÉ C·O·C·K

HUBERT TANKBANGER

Straight up with lily-of-the-valley and a hint of diesel. The only choice if you fancy a bender!

FALLEN MADONNA

If you fancy a hint of ripe melon, this is your idea of heaven. Fruity and spicey, full-bodied and irresistibly seductive. Large cups. Serves several. Beware of imitations!

FLYING HELMET

A house special! Decorated with wet celery, beaten with an egg whisk, 'fruity', 'tart,' but be warned—this one's heavy on the wallet!

René t·a·i·l·s

APERITIF

What my wife's mother keeps in the glass by her bed. Heavy on the gin, strong on the nose.

HIMMLER SUNRISE

Lashings of tequila, a squeeze of orange, a pinch of salt, crushed ice and chopped nuts. Served with a twist!

RUSSIAN FRONT

An aquired taste, with plenty of ice.

PINK PANZER

Make tracks for B company's favourite snifter! Large Bols with a dash of pink. You'll be begging for another shot!

I was just reflecting earlier today that the old undertaker with the dicky ticker has not been sniffing around the café recently. Not since he sank a litre of embalming fluid by mistake on New Year's Eve and got thoroughly pickled.

I knew it was too good to last.

Yvette had just arranged a secret assignation* with me in the larder. We embraced, as heroes of the Resistance often do.

'Oh René,' she said, 'put around me your strong arms. Crush this yearning out of me. Put your rough cheek against mine. Run your rough hands through my hair. Press your rough lips to my lips. I would do anything for you.'

'Next time you go to the chemist, could you get for me a pot of skin cream?' I quipped.†

At that moment Monsieur Alfonse, the undertaker, entered the room.

'Monsieur!' he bellowed. 'What is this I see before me? The fiancé of the woman I love locked in the arms of another? Of a serving girl?'

'There is an explanation,' I said, thinking fast.

'To think that I have suppressed my desire for that adorable woman out of respect for your bravery and honour, and all the time you are doing a number behind her back! I shall go to her. And be warned, Monsieur, the gloves are off and I shall press my suit.'

'You will probably make a better job of it than she

---

* Assignment.

† There are a number of such exchanges throughout the diaries, and I can only assume that there is more to all this than meets the eye. My mother tells me that the clandestine nature of their meetings often led to some confusion, but that on this occasion she was ready for action and he, quite uncharacteristically, did not feel up to it.

would,' I said, attempting to lighten the atmosphere.

'I intend to tell her what I have seen,' he said, heading for the door.

'But Monsieur Alfonse,' I said reasonably, 'Frenchmen do not tell on other Frenchmen . . .'

'This is true,' he replied. 'But I have Belgian blood on my mother's side.'

Oh heck. Something tells me that the knockwurst is really going to hit the fan.

23 JANUARY

Lieutenant Gruber came in early yesterday evening. He was looking very frustrated. I hoped it didn't have anything to do with me.

'Your usual, Lieutenant?' I assumed he was there to enjoy a snifter.

'Ah René,' he replied, 'I . . . Goodness, that is a very exciting perfume you are wearing.'

'In fact it is my aftershave,' I explained. 'It is a cologne for men.'

'No doubt that is why I am attracted to it. Can you bend over a little?'

Things looked as though they were about to get out of hand.

'I wish to speak with you confidentially,' the Lieutenant said. 'I am having a terrible time. It is the Italian.'

'The one whose picture is in your locket?'

'No, Bertorelli. Luckily the Colonel is sympathetic. He says the man does nothing but hang around the office and get in his hair.'

'But Lieutenant,' I said, 'the Colonel has very little hair.'

'Bertorelli is very persistent. And for me it is even worse. We share a billet.'

I raised my eyebrows. 'What does he get into of yours?'

'I'll have you know, René, that Captain Bertorelli will never be seen inside the uniform of an officer of the Tank Corps. And that goes particularly for B Company.'

'So where do I fit in?' I asked, wishing I hadn't.

'Colonel Von Strohm wants you to get the Resistance to blow him up.'

'That seems a little drastic.'

The Lieutenant nodded. 'Exactly what I said.'

'And?'

'Well, the Colonel decided that you should *almost* blow him up – you know, just enough to make him a nervous wreck so that he can be sent home.'

'My wife's singing might do the trick,' I suggested.

'Oh René, I knew I could count on you. I'll have his bags brought over to the café immediately.'

What-a mistake-a to make-a.

24 JANUARY

Bertorelli arrived just before breakfast. It is not going to be easy having him around. As Lieutenant Gruber warned me, he is an insufferable bore who spends the whole time boasting about his bravery and his conquests with women.*

If it wasn't for the fact that he is constantly wooing my wife Edith, I'd write him off as the sort of man who gives cowardice a bad name. I must console myself with the eight thousand francs he will be paying per night, and

---

* *This would have been especially offensive to a man for whom discretion was the better part of valour.*

the knowledge that Hubert can now concentrate on the forgeries in his chambers without fear of interruption.

We will of course risk his finding out about the radio in the bedroom of my wife's mother, but we heroes of the Resistance have learned to live with the constant fear of discovery. And besides, anyone who goes poking around in the bedroom of my wife's mother will get a lot more than he bargained for. I don't know how that old fool Leclerc keeps doing it.

25 JANUARY

I sent the increasingly ancient forger, Leclerc, out to replenish our dwindling stocks of gin this morning.

'How shall I disguise myself?' he asked.

'You will not need a disguise,' I said, exasperated. 'Go as yourself – as a perfectly normal idiot.'

In his absence I resolved to contact London and ask them when General de Gaulle, the tall one with the big hooter, would be sending my medals. While I was transmitting, Colonel Von Strohm and Lieutenant Gruber entered the café, and I thought I heard Captain Bertorelli coming up the stairs. As ever, I was able to keep my nerve. Wrenching the radio from its mountings in a single decisive movement, I hurled it out of the window. It landed on Leclerc, who was returning from his errand, but sadly it hit him on the head. As a result he is still absolutely all right.

General de Gaulle (the tall one with the big hooter) promises René that his medals are in the post.

1 FEBRUARY

As I served him and the Colonel lunch, Bertorelli showed me the special gift that Mussolini wished him to confer upon General Von Klinkerhoffen.

'It is the Italian War Hero Medal,' he beamed.

'I don't believe I've ever seen one before,' I said.

'I think they are very rare,' the Colonel said.

Talking about medals reminds me. Mine have still not arrived. However, Michelle of the Resistance appeared in the back room as Yvette and I were deciding upon the evening's menu. Michelle is still completely obsessed with me, so I felt I had to offer her a nibble. She told me that she had already eaten.

'Then what are you doing here in broad daylight?' I asked.

'Listen very carefully,' she said. 'I shall say this only once. A new radio has arrived for you. It will be delivered by a man disguised as a mountaineer.'

'But the nearest mountain is one hundred miles away,' I pointed out patiently.

'He is lost,' she said. 'Naturally he will come in here for directions.'

'Naturally,' I said.

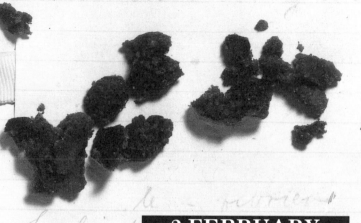

2 FEBRUARY

Lieutenant Gruber came into the bar at about nine. I asked Mimi to pour him his usual, and reminded her of my little house rule about not killing people on the premises. I also reminded her of the Lieutenant's artistic leanings, and the fact that many of those leanings were in my direction.

'Who is to blame him?' she whispered hoarsely. 'You have a quality that is irresistible. From the moment I saw you my lips hungered for your lips.'

'Here,' I said, rather hurriedly handing her a slice of ripe brie. 'Practise on this. I am rather busy.'

'Will you join me for a little snifter, René?' Hubert said.

'I've only got time for a drink, I'm afraid,' I replied. 'How are you getting on with the paintings?'

'I am forging ahead, René, but it is quite a task. The Fallen Madonna is very demanding.'

'Yes,' I said. 'You can see it in her smile.'

'And in her . . .'

'Yes,' I agreed. 'Those too.'

Nouvion 1941
A year of ups and downs.

My agent called to offer me another big part.

Hope I'm in the running.

I'm gonna wash that man right out of mein Herr.

I did it my way.

Here's goggling at your, kid.

3 FEBRUARY

The Colonel was waiting outside the café as I opened for business.

'I have arranged to meet my assistant here, René. I just wanted to remind you that he knows nothing of the British airmen, or the paintings, or the cuckoo clock.'

'I had forgotten about the cuckoo clock,' I said.

'Nor does he know about my ventures upstairs with the girls,' he continued, with a nod towards Yvette.

'With the flying helmet and the wet celery?' she asked.

'Do not mention the flying helmet and the wet celery.'

I nodded. 'Rely on us Colonel. But wouldn't life be a lot simpler if you just sent him back to Italy?'

'Undoubtedly,' he sighed. 'But Hitler still insists that an Itie unit will be coming with us when we invade England.'

'When is the invasion?' Yvette asked. 'I thought it had been cancelled.'

The Colonel looked flustered. 'Invasion? I should never have told you. Forget it.'

'Yes,' I said. 'Forget it, Yvette. Never mention the invasion or the fact that the Colonel told you about it. By the way, Colonel, we are running out of butter and sugar and paraffin and cigarettes.'

Captain Bertorelli arrived as the Colonel was taking down quantities.

'Colonnello! You my friend and I keep-a you waiting. But you forgive-a me, no?' He kissed the Colonel on both cheeks.

'Patron!' He kissed me on both cheeks.

'Pretty lady!' He kissed Yvette on both cheeks.

'Lieutenant!' He shook Gruber's hand.

At that moment I caught sight of the old forger Leclerc trying to come through the front door. With a rucksack, fifty metres of rope and an ice-pick to carry, it wasn't easy.

'Good evening,' he croaked. 'Can anybody help an old mountaineer who has lost his way?'

'Oh my God. Come here old mountaineer and tell me your problem.' My problem was that I should have thrown *him* out of the window instead of the radio.

'It is I, Leclerc.'

I suggested that this was abundantly clear to all but the totally blind.

'In the pack on my back is a new radio. It is already connected up to the batteries, and this ice-pick is the aerial.'

At that moment the rucksack started to play 'Somebody Stole My Girl' and then produced a series of static emissions of which even my wife's mother would have been proud.

Since the silly old fool was too exhausted to climb the stairs I had to sit him next to Bertorelli, hand him a bowl of soup and hope for the best.

The emissions continued.

Bertorelli, not knowing quite how to react, complimented Leclerc on the quality of his coat.

'It is a windcheater,' the bogus mountaineer corrected him.

The Itie spoke for them all: 'Whatever you do don't-a take it off-a.'

4 FEBRUARY

Yvette and I took the opportunity of spending an hour or so together in the back room this afternoon. I thought it was high time we got familiar

with the new   book

all sorts of different things to learn.*

Our session was interrupted by Michelle of the Resistance.

'Listen carefully,' she said, 'I shall say this only once.'

'What?' I asked.

'I shall say this only once,' she repeated.

'No,' I said, 'What will you say?'

'We have found a way of discovering what goes on in the dungeon of Herr Flick of the Gestapo.'

'But Michelle,' I said, 'there are some things even a Frenchman does not want to know.'

* *Fragments of this conversation will remain forever shrouded by Christmas pudding. It is quite clear, however, that René and my mother were examining the new code book very closely, each absolutely determined to crack it.*

'We have information that the Gestapo are now convinced there is a plot to blow up Hitler.'

Well, that would mean one less forgery of the Fallen Madonna with the Big Boobies for Hubert Gruber to worry about. 'Have you placed within the dungeon a listening device?'

'It was not necessary. Von Smallhausen forgot his keys yesterday and blew the door off with some Gestapo dynamite. As a result it is possible to hear everything Herr Flick says from down the corridor.'

The bravest café-owner in all France explains to a disappointed Hitler that the Fallen Madonna with the Big Boobies must remain in French hands.

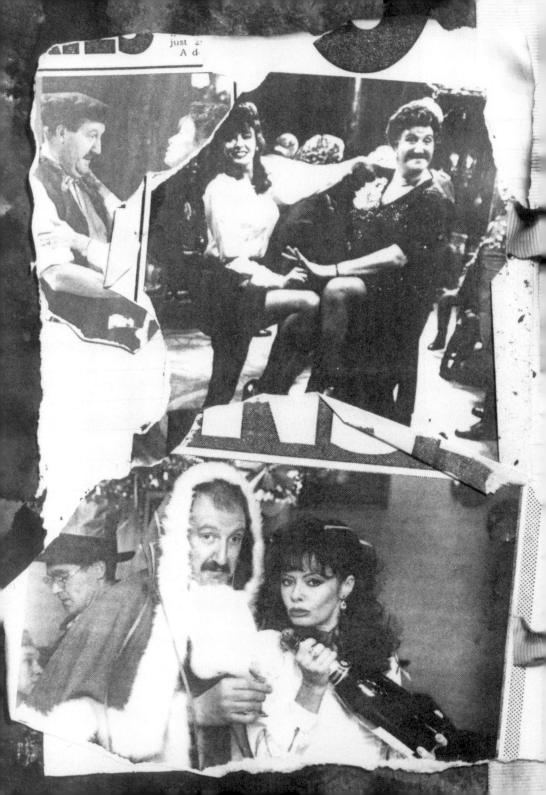

Shortly after the war René Artois filled the office of Mayor of Nouvion.
My mother says this surprised nobody; it was a very small office. During
his first term, however, there was a scandalous attempt to undermine
his reputation by implications in the local press that Yvette, who had
been taken on as a Town Hall researcher, had had 'relations' with a
string of powerful and not always salubrious men.

Fortunately, René was able to put an end to these ludicrous rumours by
explaining that Yvette was a professional, and had been working
undercover at the time.

10 FEBRUARY

I was just finishing off my boiled egg and soldiers in the back room this morning when I heard the old undertaker with the dicky ticker apologise to Yvette in the bar for his behaviour the other day.

'I am so consumed with jealousy,' he said, 'I am forgetting how we Frenchmen have this great tradition of having it off like rabbits.'

I listened more closely, wondering if his change of tone meant that I was off the hook. Just then, Edith came down the stairs. I held my breath.

'Dear lady,' he began, 'I think of you day and night. Even when I am embalming, it is your face that haunts me through the fluid.'

I knew the feeling. The same thing happens to me when I am boiling up goat's head soup.

'I can no longer contain my passion. I must kiss those tempting, sensuous lips.'

'Oh Monsieur Alfonse,' came the reply. 'You are very naughty. But, as you put it so nicely, you can have one little peck.'

There was a gasp, followed by a muffled thud as the undertaker's ticker failed to take the strain and he hit the floor. If my wife's lips are capable of putting such a burden on a man's big muscle, I reflected, it was just as well she had withheld the rest of her. I suddenly began to see Madame Lenare's creations for our wedding-night in a rather different light.

11 FEBRUARY

We had spent the best part of the day – the part I usually like to spend in my private quarters with Yvette pressing my aprons* – attempting to revive my rival and clear the café for the evening's business. Sometimes I wish he would just go and bury himself.

As soon as Monsieur Alfonse had consumed enough of my best cognac to fuel his return home, Helga appeared. I knew it was Helga because she was dressed in Herr Flick's sinister leather coat and hat, and very little else.

Despite her engagement to Herr Flick, and a slightly excessive appetite for long periods of interrogation, Helga is good news, particularly when she is out of uniform. This seems to happen increasingly often.

'Don't tell me,' I said, 'Herr Flick has once again walked off in your clothes. He is even now trying to eavesdrop on General Von Klinkerhoffen, disguised as Irma Von Kinkenrotten, a temporary female stenographer of the opposite sex.'

Helga shook her head. 'The last time he tried that the General had him arrested and thrown in the klink. He is of the opinion that the General thinks I am a nice bit of crackling, so this time he is masquerading as my not-quite-identical twin sister from Heidelberg. He suspects that the General and the Colonel are closely involved in a plot to blow up Hitler.'

'I don't wish to know any of this,' I said cunningly.

'But René,' she said, 'don't you see? If the Colonel is

---

* *It seems extraordinary that the bravest café-owner in all France would personally supervise such a mundane task, but my mother assures me that much of what they did together was ten per cent inspiration, ninety per cent perspiration.*

tortured the Gestapo might discover that the closest anyone is going to get to the Fallen Madonna with the Big Boobies is a forgery by Lieutenant Gruber, painted from memory. And it won't stop there...'

'It never does,' I said, making a mental note to re-acquaint myself with the quickest route to the Spanish border.

13 FEBRUARY

Things have gone very quiet, I was thinking to myself this morning. Too quiet. Perhaps I should just turn my back on the life of heroism and excitement I had carved for myself in Nouvion and give someone else a go.

No sooner was I reaching for my suitcase and route map than there was a great commotion in the courtyard and Lieutenant Gruber appeared. All of a sudden, turning my back didn't seem to be a terribly good idea. Especially as his face was suffused with pleasure and a fine sheen of perspiration glistened on his upper lip.

My first thought was that he had arrived to give me my Valentine's card a day early. In fact, he had just been exercising one of the General's horses, a magnificent black stallion.

'René, there is nothing like the sight of a handsome beast with nostrils flaring, foam flying from the mouth, clattering over the cobbles scattering peasants.'

'Yes,' I said, 'I expect the horse enjoyed it too. You had better sit down, Lieutenant.'

Over a cognac, he revealed to me the true reason for his visit.

'Something rather extraordinary has happened, René.'

'I'm getting used to it,' I said.

'General Von Klinkerhoffen has placed in custody Herr Flick of the Gestapo who has been spying on him whilst in the disguise of Helga's nearly-identical twin sister from Heidelberg.'

'I don't imagine that Himmler's reaction will look too good on the General's CV.'

'He has thought of that. Herr Flick has been arrested on suspicion of being Irma Von Kinkenrotten, a temporary female secretary of the opposite sex who escaped his grasp once before.'

'It all seems fairly straightforward,' I said.

Just a little puff in the bath.

14 FEBRUARY

I have learnt to approach this particular Saint's Day with some caution, especially since Hubert Gruber returned from the Russian Front and Edith started going to night classes with Madame Lenare.

Mimi decided to celebrate by inviting Captain Bertorelli up to her room and tearing him limb from limb.

She remained technically within the limits of my little house rule, but the Itie was in bad shape when he came down for lunch.

Yvette decided to celebrate by taking me into the larder and showing me a Valentine's message that she had tattooed on to her left ▓▓▓▓▓▓ because she hadn't been able to find a card. Unfortunately I had left my reading glasses upstairs, so I had to get really close and then we

absolutely covered in Brie.*

Edith was sent a rather dog-eared heart with a big question mark on it.

'It is from a secret admirer,' she beamed.

I couldn't help feeling that it might have been from someone quite old with a dicky ticker.

Apart from that, however, very little has happened. I think I'll stop here and have an early night.

* *René often reminds us that certain things were in short supply during these dark days, even for a hero of the Resistance. Taking this into account, it still seems remarkably inventive of my mother to tattoo her message on some leftover Brie.*

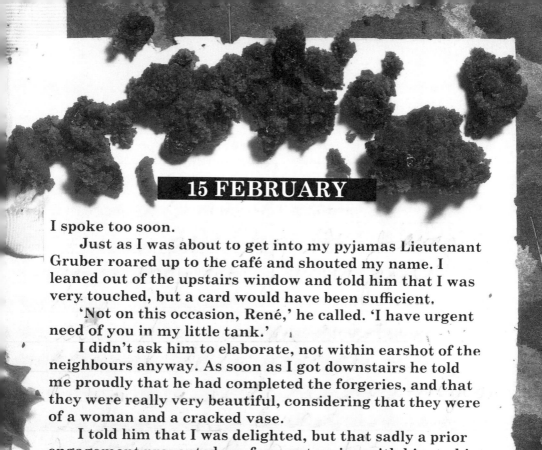

15 FEBRUARY

I spoke too soon.

Just as I was about to get into my pyjamas Lieutenant
Gruber roared up to the café and shouted my name. I
leaned out of the upstairs window and told him that I was
very touched, but a card would have been sufficient.

'Not on this occasion, René,' he called. 'I have urgent
need of you in my little tank.'

I didn't ask him to elaborate, not within earshot of the
neighbours anyway. As soon as I got downstairs he told
me proudly that he had completed the forgeries, and that
they were really very beautiful, considering that they were
of a woman and a cracked vase.

I told him that I was delighted, but that sadly a prior
engagement prevented me from returning with him to his
chambers to admire his handiwork.

I think he was a little disappointed, but I had a nagging
feeling that where boobies are concerned, there's no
substitute for the real thing. And the real thing was still
in the Nouvion West Sub Area headquarters of the
Communist Resistance.

20 FEBRUARY

I cannot say that I have missed Herr Flick's regular presence in the back room, because the Gestapo never pays its bills. Also, I have to admit, it's nice to see Helga on her own from time to time, particularly since she has not yet got all her clothes back.

I sat at her table for a moment or two and asked her how her fiancé was getting on. She told me that only that overgrown fruit-bat Von Smallhausen had been allowed in to see him.

'That must really have cheered him up,' I said.

'Yes,' said Helga. 'Herr Flick has always appreciated Von Smallhausen's sense of humour. He offered Herr Flick a suicide pill to crush between his teeth so no one would know what a fool he had made of himself.'

'I bet that went down well.'

'Herr Flick told him he was very, very stupid. Von Smallhausen replied that he, on the other hand, was not chained up in a dungeon wearing women's clothing.'

'Something tells me that it won't be long before Himmler hears of this.'

'Herr Flick has ordered Von Smallhausen to get a message to Berlin to explain his predicament.'

'It's going to take a bit of explaining,' I said.

23 FEBRUARY

It may be that Herr Flick's incarceration had something to do with the festive mood in the café this evening. The only false note was provided by Edith, who insisted on testing the mettle of her audience by singing 'It's a Long Way to Tipperary.'

'It's a long, long way to Tipperary,' she concluded after what seemed like hours, 'but my heart's right there.'

'What a pity the rest of her isn't,' the Colonel said.

As everyone gradually summoned up the courage to remove the cheese from their ears, conversation resumed.

'Come and sit with us, René,' Lieutenant Gruber entreated. 'I have brought with me the completed forgeries of the paintings.'

He placed a number of knockwurst sausages proudly on the table. They were joined more or less immediately by four or five more, deposited with his usual ceremony by the Itie, Bertorelli.

'Look-a what my mama send for us from Italy. The black-a de market salami. Take-a de sniff – is beautiful, no?'

Apparently Bertorelli's sausages were destined to be a gift for Edith as soon as the gallant Captain had been for a cut-a de hair. I hoped they might keep her off my back for a while.

No sooner had he left than that idiot Crabtree arrived with a consignment of dynamite that Michelle wanted me to store in the cellar. Honestly, that girl will go to any lengths to provide herself with an excuse to have regular liaisons with me.

Crabtree had obviously spent some time deciding upon the most original way of transporting the explosives without arousing suspicion.

'Good moaning,' he said, as he eased his way delicately towards the bar. 'The deenamote is inside the sisages.'

'Thank you, Officer, you could not have come at a better time,' I said, showing him the door.

I had hardly had time to count the sausages when Mimi alerted us to the fact that General Von Klinkerhoffen was heading in our direction. Luckily we were able to hide every single one down the front of Lieutenant Gruber's trousers and Helga's bosom. The evening was full of surprises.

25 FEBRUARY

I had always known that tampering with the front of Lieutenant Gruber's trousers would have drastic repercussions, but I was not prepared to be dragged from my bed early yesterday morning and frogmarched to the German Headquarters.

When I was hurled through the door of the Colonel's office I saw that both Helga and Lieutenant Gruber were with him. One look at their faces told me that they were under a lot of pressure from General Von Klinkerhoffen. That usually meant one of two things. Either we would all test out the effectiveness of the escape route to Switzerland, or I would be shot. And since I did not have the original canvas of The Fallen Madonna with the Big Boobies to bargain with, it looked like Goodnight Nouvion.

'René,' Lieutenant Gruber said fiercely, 'we are very cross with you.'

'Yes, René,' the Colonel spat. 'You have a lot of explaining to do. We have examined the sausages and it is clear to us that you are working for the Resistance again.'

'The two concealed down my bosom were dynamite,' Helga said, somewhat unnecessarily.

'And supposing I'd got something hot down the front of my trousers?' Lieutenant Gruber asked.

I looked from one to another. 'There is no answer to that.'

'The dynamite would have exploded – and I have not even made a will!'

'You would have died intestate,' I said.

There was an uneasy silence.

'I think we should forget all this nonsense about me being the bravest Resistance Leader in all France,' I bluffed, 'and spend a bit of time sorting out which knockwurst is which.'

'I agree, René,' said Hubert. 'Perhaps you could give me a hand with these . . .'

Thankfully we had the whole lot lined up on the Colonel's desk without too much fuss.

Lieutenant Gruber put an end to the confusion: 'Those are the forgeries of The Cracked Vase with the Big Daisies by Van Gogh which are to go to the General, one of which he will send to Hitler believing it is a forgery, and one of which he will keep himself believing it is a genuine Van Gogh, but which of course is a forgery. Those others are the forgeries of The Fallen Madonna with the Big Boobies by Van Clomp which were to go to Herr Flick, of which he would have sent one to Hitler, and the other he would have kept himself believing it to be the original which he will sell after the war, but which of course is also a forgery, and anyway he does not need either at the moment.'

'Why is this?' I asked.

'Because Herr Flick is in the nick,' the Colonel said.

'What for?' I asked innocently.

'For spying on me and the General, wearing Helga's clothes.'

I wanted to ask what he and the General were doing in Helga's clothes, but on this occasion discretion was the better part of valour.

I made my way back to the inevitable hero's welcome at the café. Since the Colonel wanted the forgeries returned to their hiding place in my cellar, I had a great many knockwurst down the front of my trousers. Something in Yvette's and Mimi's expressions told me that they could see how pleased I was to be back with them.

Always a great respecter of tradition, it appears that René was planning on reviving the coat-of-arms of the Barons Artois of Nouvion, to whom he claimed to be directly related.

Experts will note the imaginative employment of a number of arcane heraldic devices, including the three knockwursts rampant and the wet celery dormant.

11 MARCH

Despite appearances, I was not ready to get immediately back into action. I wasn't in the mood for writing much either.

So another fortnight has passed. I thought occasionally of Herr Flick, chained spread-eagled in the château dungeon, especially when Mimi pinned me down in the cellar and demanded a rise. That girl is very trying. It is no time at all since she replaced Maria, and already she is impossible to satisfy. I spent some time explaining how difficult things are for me at the moment and then just had to put my foot down and tell her she couldn't have one.

Apart from anything else, how would Yvette feel?

12 MARCH

Helga has been thinking of Herr Flick too. Apart from anything else, he is still dressed in her underwear.

She had five minutes with him this afternoon.

'Was that enough?' I asked.

'Not at all,' she replied wistfully. 'He is in such an unusual position. It is very painful for him. But it is also instructive. I think he is taking notes.'

'Could you do nothing for him?'

'I asked him how I could relieve his situation. He told me he could not endure the agony in his legs and demanded a pair of scissors.'

'It would take a while for him to cut through his chains

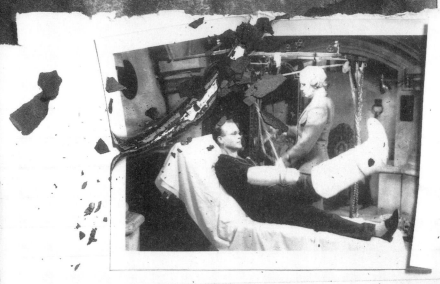

Herr Flick attempts to get his leg over.

with those,' I said, as one who has often thought of trying nonetheless.

She shook her head.

'He wanted to cut through his tight knicker elastic.'

At that instant four of my best glasses shattered behind the bar. I thought Denise and her friends were paying us another visit, but no such luck. Edith had started singing.

'Always have ready a dustpan and brush at times like this,' I chided Mimi.

Yvette signalled me to move through for a secret meeting in the back room.

'Who wants me?' I asked as I shut the door.

'I do,' she said.

I've got to hand it to Yvette. There was a time when Michelle was taking much of the initiative in our undercover work, but these days the balls are definitely back in Yvette's court.

'Do you not ache for some action at such moments as this?' she whispered.

'I am occasionally a bit stiff,' I replied, 'but I put it down to age.'

15 MARCH

Needless to say, it wasn't long before we saw the sort of action Yvette yearned for.

Last night Michelle of the Resistance tapped like a phantom on the window of the back room. Monsieur Alfonse was with her.

'I brought this intrepid lady here in the back of my small hearse with the small horse,' he explained.*

'Monsieur,' I said, 'if she is discovered you could be shot.'

'I know, but it is worth it.'

'He does this for France,' Michelle said.

'And three hundred francs a mile plus waiting time,' Monsieur Alfonse reminded her.

'I will pay him only once,' Michelle said.

She was there to warn us that Himmler is not pleased about Herr Flick's disappearance, and we can all expect a big stink. The General has wind of this, and has ordered the Colonel and the Lieutenant to disguise themselves as members of the Resistance and help Herr Flick escape. They will then lead him into an ambush.

Monsieur Alfonse left the small hearse with the small horse to Edith in his will. She used it to do the shopping.

16 MARCH

'There is only one problem, René,' the Colonel said as he gave me their version. 'To ensure that we are not shot along with Herr Flick we have to wear a small cornflower in our hats.'

'I think that sunflowers would give us a better chance,' the Lieutenant said.

I'd be tempted to take along an entire bush.

19 MARCH

I've had a very nasty feeling about Herr Flick's position for some time. I now know why.

I was foolish enough to be attracted by Helga as she sat by the fountain this afternoon. I can't quite get used to the fact that she is still missing many of her clothes.

'Sit here,' she said, pointing beside her.

'I do not wish to be seen in the square fraternising,' I said.

'How would you like to be seen dead?' she asked.

I shrugged. Girls had chatted me up like this many times before. I always gave the same answer.

'I will fraternise.'

'Herr Flick is close to cracking. If he does so he may spill the beans about the forgeries of the Fallen Madonna with the ...'

'Dynamite bosom?' I suggested, eyeing what lay behind Herr Flick's sinister leather lapels.

She nodded. 'Gruber will be next. He will implicate us, the trail will lead to you and you will be shot.'

'Thank you for warning me. I will leave at once for the Spanish border on that idiot policeman's bicycle.'

'You would not get ten yards,' she said.

'Why not?'

'Because I can shoot ten yards.'

'How can I help?' I asked.

29 MARCH

I shouldn't have asked.

Before you could say 'sinister leather overcoat' I was on my way to the château with Helga and Von Smallhausen to rescue Herr Flick. My moustache was newly trimmed, my glasses newly appropriated from my wife's mother.

You've guessed it. Even though I am shorter than Himmler, fatter than Himmler, younger than Himmler, balder than Himmler and cannot speak German, I was masquerading as Heinrich Himmler.

Worse was to come.

René Artois' Nouvion was the greatest bestseller in all France in the late 1940s. The map which follows was folded into the Christmas pudding, and appears to be an early draft of a feature he intended to include. My mother tells me it depicts some of René's favourite walks.

30 MARCH

I was in the back of the sinister Gestapo staff car with Von Smallhausen. Helga drove.

'What do I do if anyone speaks to me?' I asked.

'Hit them with your whip,' she said.

I was just thinking of practising on Von Smallhausen when a bullet richocheted past my newly trimmed moustache. I must admit I was unnerved. We heroes of the Resistance are often shot at, but only occasionally by our own side.

As a result, I was almost glad when we arrived at the General's Headquarters and I was able to calm myself by whipping a few guards who were impertinent enough to greet me. But not for long. As soon as we entered Herr Flick's cell, the rescue plan took a sinister turn. Herr Flick ordered Von Smallhausen to hand over his gun and used it to persuade me to take off my clothes. Helga told me that when he was in that sort of mood it was better to strip first and ask questions later.

Suffice it to say that not long afterwards Herr Flick had made good his escape disguised as Heinrich Himmler, leaving me chained to a pillar in Helga's underwear. Sadly, there was no room in them for Helga as well.

31 MARCH

The Colonel and the Lieutenant arrived moments later,
disguised as Gestapo. They both wore sinister leather coats
and hats, but surprisingly it was Von Strohm who had the
limp.

'René,' the Lieutenant greeted me. 'You are the last
person we expected to see, especially dressed like that –
not that it doesn't suit you.'

'I have been double-crossed,' I said.

'I can see that,' Hubert replied. 'And your stockings
are wrinkled.'

1 APRIL

This is no joke. The memory of those hours as a prisoner
still returns to haunt me as I write. I find I simply cannot
keep it up. Yvette, particularly, is generous with her
support,* but only time will tell whether I can fully
recover.

---

* *I myself have often had reason to be grateful for this sort of support*
from my editor.

2 APRIL

Lieutenant Gruber returned much later with the keys to my wrist irons. As he released me he expressed his hope that I would soon be able to remove the experience from my memory.

I hope he will have more success than I have had.

3 APRIL

I suppose I can't complain. At least I've had no trouble from the idiot British airmen recently. They've spent almost two months living in the dustbins outside the windows of the back room.

I must say I wouldn't fancy living off the stale bread and mouldy potato peel that Leclerc covers them with from time to time, but they don't seem to mind. They pop out occasionally to use the pissoir, but only to post letters.

Monsieur Alfonse, on the other hand, is still getting right up my nose, and it's not just the embalming fluid. I

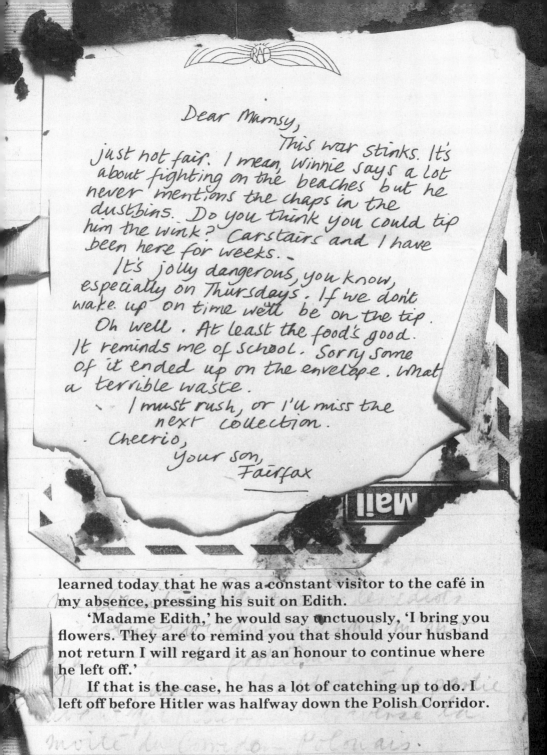

Dear Mumsy,

This war stinks. It's just not fair. I mean, Winnie says a lot about fighting on the beaches but he never mentions the chaps in the dustbins. Do you think you could tip him the wink? Carstairs and I have been here for weeks.

It's jolly dangerous, you know, especially on Thursdays. If we don't wake up on time we'll be on the tip.

Oh well. At least the food's good. It reminds me of school. Sorry some of it ended up on the envelope. What a terrible waste.

I must rush, or I'll miss the next collection.

Cheerio,
Your son,
Fairfax

learned today that he was a constant visitor to the café in my absence, pressing his suit on Edith.

'Madame Edith,' he would say unctuously, 'I bring you flowers. They are to remind you that should your husband not return I will regard it as an honour to continue where he left off.'

If that is the case, he has a lot of catching up to do. I left off before Hitler was halfway down the Polish Corridor.

10 APRIL

That idiot Crabtree assures me that I should be grateful that the RAF are still farting for freedom, and in a way I am.

As I selflessly attempted with my torch to direct their bombs away from my loved ones and towards the café-owner with a bigger one across the square, I came upon Yvette trembling in a doorway.

'Big bangs frighten me,' she said.

'It is only natural,' I replied.

We were almost immediately interrupted by Edith, who has been known to put even a squadron of Wellingtons to flight. I don't know how many times I've had to explain how Yvette's duty at a time like this is to shield the body of the bravest man in all France from rogue shrapnel, but tonight makes one more.

11 APRIL

As dawn broke, I realised that last night's air-raid has left us with bad news and good news.

The bad news is that the café-owner across the square is still very much in business. The good news is that we seem to have got rid of the British airmen.

12 APRIL

It is too much to hope that their own side dropped a very large bomb on them, but I'm keeping my fingers crossed.

13 APRIL

It was too much.

However, they are out of my hair. They've given themselves up to the local policeman, who is himself a British agent in disguise, and should therefore have the responsibility of organising their return to England.

14 APRIL

They're back in my hair.

Crabtree has released them on the grounds of insufficient evidence.

15 APRIL

And if that's not enough, I've got to put my head back in the den of Denise Laroque, the fanatical ex-lion tamer, in order to repossess the original canvases of the Fallen Madonna with the Big Boobies and the Cracked Vase with the Big Daisies.

I have to do this because Herr Flick wants them, because the General wants them, because the Colonel wants them, and because Hitler still wants to give one to Eva for her birthday. And because if I don't I will be shot.

Since discovering that Denise is due to go to a Communist Resistance fund-raising dinner in Brest in a week's time, I have also experienced a revival in my ambition to see the Fallen Madonna safely into French hands.

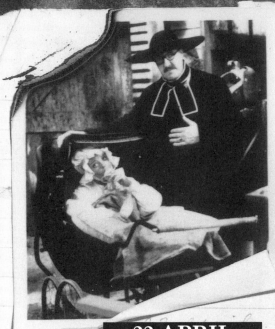

22 APRIL

It is possible that one or two people were a little surprised to see the bravest café-owner in all France dressed as a Roman Catholic vicar wheeling a pram through the countryside. Poor Yvette, I know, was positively beside herself. I think she probably knows that vicars only have very small stipends, and was worried about how long I would be able to keep it up.

Why exactly *was* I dressed as a Roman Catholic vicar wheeling a pram with Mimi Labonq inside it dressed as a baby? It is a good question, and the answer is simple. Mimi's nappy was covering something that is very special and dear to me, an object of beauty that I am hoping will bring much joy and comfort to a retired café-owner in his old age. I could hardly wait to get her home and run my hands over it again.*

---

* *Rene refers, of course, to the painting of the Fallen Madonna with the Big Boobies by Van Clomp. Somehow the Cracked Vase with the Big Daisies by Van Gogh never held the same allure for him.*

23 APRIL

I didn't get home.

It is the early hours of the morning and there is no one in the deserted sawmill but me and my alarmingly devoted serving girl. Is there time, I wonder, for a quick entry?

I think I'll chance it. The Colonel and the Itie with the dead chicken on his head were supposed to create a diversion so that I could make off with the paintings. But, knowing them, they have probably been ambushed by the Communist Resistance and captured, and even at this moment are being brought here at gunpoint by Denise Laroque, the fanatical head of the Communist Resistance (Nouvion West Sub Area) who is as madly in love with me as ever.

Ah . . .*

---

* *Always ready for action, René had brought his diary with him –*
disguised, perhaps, as a Bible. But after all the excitement, there
does not seem to have been enough lead left in his pencil for what he
had in mind.

20 MAY

I was right.

Lieutenant Gruber, Colonel Von Strohm, Leclerc and the odious Itie were bundled into the room before I'd even finished my sentence.

It didn't looked good for any of us, but luckily it looked absolutely terrible for Leclerc in particular. The girls from the Communist Resistance suspected him of leading the Germans to their secret hideout. They told him they wanted to take him outside and put him up against a wall.

The silly old fool thought he'd got lucky. Then the truth dawned on him.

'He made me do it,' he blustered, pointing at the Colonel. 'I would die for France.'

'Then why didn't you?' Denise asked reasonably.

Leclerc paused.

'I will eventually . . .'

As a man of the cloth it was clearly up to me to intercede on behalf of the frail old piano-tuning peasant. But how could I best persuade them to spare his life? I decided to tell them the truth.

'He has the mind of a five-year-old,' I said. 'He has a condition known in the medical world as "gaga".'

What happened next surprised us all. Captain Bertorelli, despite being Italian, and an Italian in the Italian army to boot, stepped boldly forward to face the guns. Perhaps he mistook them for ice-cream cones. I've suspected his eyesight since he first called my wife beautiful.

'Why you so damned aggressive, eh?' he asked. 'You should not make-a the war, you should make-a the love.'

'Does anyone fancy this Italian before we shoot him?' Denise asked.

'He could be quite amusing for an hour or two,' said a girl whose body had up until then been hidden by one of the barn doors, but only just.

'I want-a to make-a the last request,' said Bertorelli.

'I must have-a the blindfold.'

'Before you are shot?' Denise asked.

'No. Before I make-a the love . . .'

It was time for someone brave and fearless to take charge and suggest that we could get for the Germans a large ransom.

'We are all good Communists,' I said masterfully. 'Let us form a committee and have a debate and put a motion on the table. You need party funds – you could start a newspaper and advertise for members.'

Denise agreed with me. Girls often do. They find my ideas penetrating.

René Artois, seconds away from becoming two of the bravest men in all France.

21 MAY

I have often heard Herr Flick say how good Helga is down in his dungeon for a bit of

other,

screwing   slap and tickle

Favourite

explosive   how   your father?*
He also spends a lot of time watching other people in
action. Apparently he had had me under strict

---

* *Another passage that has been rendered obscure by Christmas*
pudding. Nonetheless I have used my increasingly detailed
knowledge of the participants to piece together the missing portions
of text as follows:
'dungeon for a bit of interrogation about some misdemeanour or other.
The interrogation might entail some thumb-screwing, and failure to
answer the questions would result in the use of the old slap and tickle
technique. Favourite questions to Resistance members would include:
Where does your mother keep the explosives, and how about your
father?'

surveillance as I wheeled Mimi's pram towards the sawmill. Helga was dressed as a nursemaid and Herr Flick as a baby in a pram. He wore a sinister black leather bonnet, and a nappy with little blue swastikas on it.

'Can you see anything through your powerful Gestapo binoculars, Herr Flick?' Helga asked him.

'The Colonel, the Lieutenant and the Italian Captain are surrounded by rough working-class women with guns. We must assume that their plans have failed.'

'What do we do now?'

'Wheel me back to my headquarters – and do not go over any bumps as I wish to go to the potty.'

Herr Flick's knob is so big...

...that he sometimes needs to keep it in a sling.

22 MAY

The idiot policeman gave Edith and Yvette the massage that I had been kiptured by the Kimmunist Resostance.

'No!' Yvette screamed, grasping at once the enormity of my predicament.*

Crabtree pulled out a small bottle from beneath his cape.

'Put these smelling silts under your neese and have a good sniff.'

But Yvette need not have worried. I have trained Michelle well. My protegée announced that she had a brilliant plan.

* Predicament.

23 MAY

Brilliant. She only wanted to call in the RAF from London and have their bombers drop bombs on a sawmill not a million kilometres from where I was standing.

She said the hated Germans and the Communists were together under one roof, and I would be proud to die for France. And so I shall – in good time. Meanwhile I fully intend to live for France. Heroes of the Resistance are in short supply in the Nouvion area, so my particular qualities of leadership and courage are rarely seen.

Monsieur Alfonse took a different view.

'He will die a happy man,' the eager embalmer said to Edith, 'knowing that I will marry you, dear lady, and look after you tenderly for the few years remaining to me before leaving to you the very large quantity of money in my Swiss bank account – the number of which I will reveal just before we blow out the candle on the night of our honeymoon.'

24 MAY

The girls at last agreed that I should be allowed to go and try to get a ransom for the prisoners. One million francs for the Germans seems to be the going rate, and ten tins of baked beans for the Itie. That sounded fair – especially as baked beans are on special offer at the butcher with the big chopper.

Before I set off on my dangerous mission, the Colonel made me retrieve the paintings from their hiding place behind the beam. Little did he realise they were forgeries; the real ones, by this time, were warm and snug in the nappy of Mimi Labonq. But I was happy to humour him.

'Put them down Gruber's trousers,' the Colonel said.

I hesitated.

'Would you like them on the left or the right, Lieutenant?' I asked.

'I think, if it is all the same to you, one each side.'

Poor Lieutenant Gruber. I hadn't seen him look so ill at ease since he heard that one of his pals from his window-dressing days had been hit in the Bulge.

'Despite my experience in the touching-up of old masters, I had not formerly realised how coarse was the canvas used by Van Gogh.'

'He probably painted it on the skirt of some old native,' I said.

'Let us hope he washed it first,' the Lieutenant replied.

Denise bade me farewell as I set off on my mission, but not before she had delivered a word of warning to the prisoners.

'If the ransom is paid you will be released more or less unharmed,' she snarled. 'If not – bang, bang, bang.'

They wouldn't let me take baby Mimi with me. They said it was better that the poor child be looked after by women.

'But surely she will get in the way when you are killing Germans and blowing things up?' I said.

Denise would have none of it. 'The worry of being an orphan has already made her look old beyond
her years.'

1 JUNE

General von Klinkerhoffen doesn't want to pay the ransom.

My first thought was: If he does not care, why should I? Let there be banging. My second thought was: If there is a lot of banging, there might also be a lot of Big Boobies with holes in them, and Cracked Vases that are more or less impossible to stick back together.

2 JUNE

Michelle cannot stop the bombers. The battery on the radio is flat. We shall have to find the ransom money from somewhere else – or I'll never be able to provide for my o⬛⬛age.*

3 JUNE

I've thought of somewhere else.

Edith has been despatched to borrow all the money in Monsieur Alfonse's Swiss bank account.

4 JUNE

First the bad news. Monsieur Alfonse did not die from the shock.

Now the even worse news. Suddenly he cannot remember the number of his account and the Swiss bank is closed anyway because it is a bank holiday.

How else can we raise the money? Not even Roger Leclerc could forge one million francs by tomorrow. Not

---

*   Unkind critics – and it has to be said that the great man had more
    than his fair share of knockers – might interpret this piece of exploded
    text as 'old age'. As if René would think of protecting his own interests
    at a time like this. The intended word is clearly 'orphanage'. My
    mother told me he never rested in his pursuit of the interests of the
    younger generation. It is extraordinary that he never had children of
    his own.

good ones, anyway.*

Michelle has a plan that she will outline to me tomorrow for my approval. I am proud of that girl. She has learnt much from the master.

The maître heartily recommends the Boeuf René aux Flageolets to a grateful customer.

There seems to be some confusion here. The billion lire note as shown is of course genuine.

5 JUNE

'I am not going to rob a bank,' I said when she had finished.
'I could get life – or even longer. And then where would
everyone be?'

They were too upset by the question to answer
immediately.

'In that case we will not get back the paintings and we
will be poor forever,' Edith said at length.

'René,' Yvette winked, 'think of the uses you will have
for this money ...'

12 JUNE

There we were then, outside the bank. The church clock
had just struck twelve. Michelle was keeping watch.
Should anyone approach she would hoot like an owl.
Personally I think that as leader it was I that should have
been doing the hooting, and she the breaking in. But there
is a time to lead and a time to stand back, and anyway it
was a bit windy so I decided it would be warmer inside.

13 JUNE

Let me explain where I have been for the last few days. I
have been locked inside a bank vault.

Leclerc got the door open all right, and we entered the
vault. Unfortunately the wind then blew it shut again.

'I still have the plastic explosive,' the old fool said after
we'd been there a week. 'We will blow open the door.'

I greeted his words with a mixture of relief and regret.
I would be glad to be relieved, but at the same time I was
pleased to be able to help Yvette, who suffered from
claustrophobia and needed to be held tight while she took
deep breaths.

Michelle was waiting outside with Crabtree while all this was going on.

'They have been a long time,' Michelle said at last.

'Do you think we should have a poke?' Crabtree asked.

'A poke?'

'To see what is happening.'

It was kind of them to think of rescuing us but unfortunate that they arrived exactly ten seconds after Leclerc had lit the fuse.

14 JUNE

My troops have recovered from the shock of the explosion, thanks largely to the bottle of my finest cognac they drank when we got back to the café. Personally, I felt better the moment I had counted the stolen money. I've never counted to a million before, even on a good night.

19 JUNE

A tuning-point in my life. I have decided I cannot continue to allow my wife to sing. I am losing customers. She will be heartbroken, but that's show business.

I have a plan. I fetched down my old gramophone from the attic, a box of needles – medium-loud – and a pile of records. Now all I have to do is break the news to Edith.

20 JUNE

No rush. Tomorrow will do.

21 JUNE

Or the next day.

22 JUNE

'Edith,' I said pleasantly, 'I am very worried about Monsieur Leclerc's piano-playing when he accompanies you. He does not do your voice justice.'

'I have thought this myself,' she replied.

'It occurred to me that if you were backed by an orchestra – preferably a big symphony orchestra, a loud one, conducted by Toscanini ... then your full potential could be realised.'

I handed Edith a record.

'Toscanini – how wonderful. What is this name – it looks like Jeanette MacDonald.'

I had to explain that it was just possible that the MacDonald woman was singing on it a little bit, but the customers would never notice.

'Your voices are so similar,' Yvette said.

'Of course,' Edith said. 'I model myself on her.'

Yvette started the record. I tapped the bar-top with a spoon and started to conduct.

Edith sang: 'Love is where you find it ...'

I tapped the bar-top with the spoon.

'Edith – much quieter. You are drowning sixty-four members of the New York Philharmonic.'

After several false starts I finally managed to get her to sing so pianissimo that she was scarcely audible.

'Turn your back, Yvette,' I said. 'Tell me who is singing.'

'I cannot tell. I think it is Madame Edith.'

'Perfect,' I said to Edith. 'You open next month.'

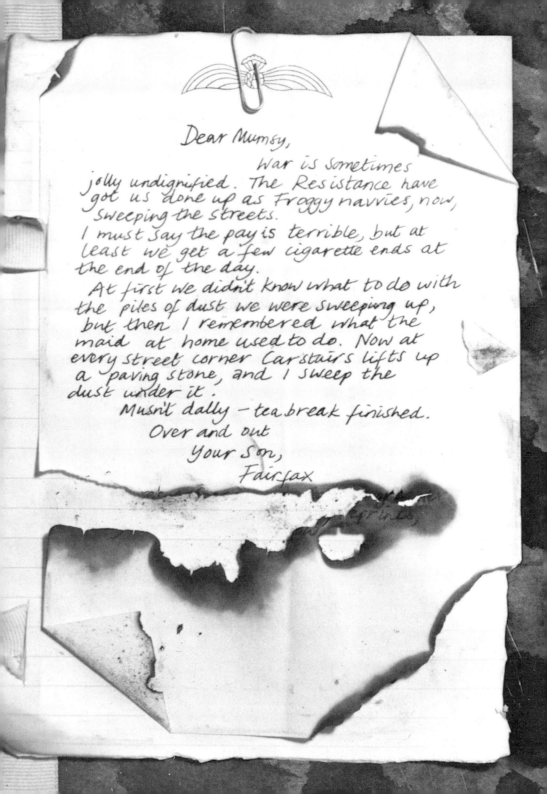

Dear Mumsy,

War is sometimes jolly undignified. The Resistance have got us done up as Froggy navvies, now, sweeping the streets.

I must say the pay is terrible, but at least we get a few cigarette ends at the end of the day.

At first we didn't know what to do with the piles of dust we were sweeping up, but then I remembered what the maid at home used to do. Now at every street corner Carstairs lifts up a paving stone, and I sweep the dust under it.

Musn't dally — tea break finished.

Over and out

Your Son,

Fairfax

Helga is not certain whether it's a gun Herr Flick has under his sinister leather coat, or if he's just pleased to see her.

Edith Artois takes a break from her act to read her next request: 'Four more slices of Emmental'.

26 JUNE

Helga tells me that Herr Flick was looking off-colour this morning. His skin had turned from its usual shade of putty to a more deathly white.

'I have just been to the bank where every Friday I collect my divi,' he told her. 'The strong room has been blown open. One million francs from my personal Gestapo slush fund have vanished without a trace.'

Oh heck, one million francs from his personal Gestapo slush fund. I started to look a little off-colour myself. Helga continued her story.

'But who would have the temerity to do such a wicked thing?' she had asked him.

'Someone who hates me.'

'Everybody hates you.'

'In the Gestapo that is a measure of one's success.'

Nevertheless, he thinks that General von

Klinkerhoffen hates him most, and suspects him of stealing the money.

'I feel very small and alone,' he told Helga. 'You will lend me fifty-seven francs for a ham sandwich and a cup of coffee.'

1 JULY

Crabtree dropped a bumshell this afternoon.

'When you ribbed the bonk there was a wetness,' he said. 'I have drawn poctures of the sispocts. Nobody has soon the poctures because I have not ponned them on the beard outside the Polooce Stootion, but some of them lurk vaguely familiar.'

This is bad nose indeed.

6 JULY

If Flick finds out that we have his money he will have us shot – slowly and painfully. But what can we do with it?

Michelle says the Resistance will look after it. I'm sure they will. We'd never see it again.

Monsieur Alfonse is prepared to conceal it in a tomb, but I am sure he means a vault in a bank in Switzerland.

The argument was settled when Colonel Von Strohm appeared in the square, heading towards the café. He looked cross. Michelle grabbed a couple of notes and vanished like a phantom into the hairdresser. I was left with the rest, and the Colonel was getting closer.

'Hide it down my bosom,' Yvette offered.

'There is no room,' I said.

'We will hide it down your trousers,' Edith said. 'There is plenty there.'

The Colonel and Lieutenant Gruber entered the café just as the last few notes were stuffed into place.

Lieutenant Gruber is bent on opening up a second front...

... and René reluctantly tries his hand at a little insider dealing.

'Colonel, Lieutenant, what a coincidence,' I said. 'We were just on our way to rescue you.'

'René,' said the Lieutenant, 'I hear a strange rustling sound.

'Mice,' I said.

'I have the strange illusion that it is coming from your trousers.'

'Would you put a mousetrap down *your* trousers Lieutenant?' I asked.

I hobbled off into the back room, unaware that the Colonel had ordered Gruber to follow me. I pulled down my trousers to release all the money, and stooped to pick it up.

'René,' I heard a voice behind me. 'Could it be that I have hit the jackpot?'

I straightened up fast, and made the Lieutenant promise that he wouldn't tell anyone what he had seen. He replied that long underwear was nothing to be ashamed of.

'I am talking about the money,' I said. 'Last night we blew up the bank and stole one million francs to pay a ransom for your release.'

Not for the first time, Gruber was touched.

'You did this for me!' he exclaimed. 'Clearly the money is not safe in your trousers. We must put it down mine. I must make room for it.'

He reached deep into his trousers until his hand hit something firm.

'I think I have found the Van Clomp,' he smiled. 'Please René, take one end of it.'

Cautiously, I held out my hand. I had no idea how big his Van Clomp was going to be. As I closed my fingers around it, I realised to my relief that it was the size of a rolled-up painting.

'I have to be very careful with the Van Gogh,' Gruber added.

'It is very valuable,' I agreed.

'It has very rough canvas.'

As I pushed it down inside my long johns I saw what he meant. We began to transfer the money to his trousers. They were exquisitely tailored, if a little tight. Apparently a dear friend from his old window-dressing days had had a hand in them.

10 JULY

This is getting complicated. I have given the money we stole from the bank to Lieutenant Gruber. He is our deadly enemy most of the time – or in my case, my deadly friend. He is taking care of the money so it cannot be traced to us. In return he has given to me what he believes to be the original paintings, except that they're not, to keep down my trousers. I will give them to Edith to put with the other forgeries.

When the Lieutenant asks for them I hope she does not give him the real ones by mistake. They, of course, are the ones in Mimi's trousers.

You have to be on the ball in this game.

14 JULY

Denise knocked on the window tonight. The Germans are looking for her everywhere. Naturally she had come to the house of the man she loves.

'But what if they find you here?' I asked.

'Then we will die in a hail of bullets, fighting together, in each other's arms.'

'Surely there is somewhere safer?' I protested. 'The bus shelter, for instance – nobody goes there – the service is discontinued.'

Café René

It seems I no longer run a café; I am the proprietor of a refuge for girls on the run. This is not as much fun as it sounds: they are girls of the Communist Resistance.

Miss Denise Laroque, whose description is no doubt being circulated throughout the length and breadth of the country, is hiding in the room of Mimi Labonq, who hates Communists but has accepted my explanation that the fugitive has Militant Conservative tendencies.

Louise, her deputy, is also hidden in my café, despite my protests that I am a bit full at the moment.

'Could you not come back next week?' I asked, quite reasonably.

'There are Germans everywhere. If I have to die, let it be in your arms.'

Of course. How else would a girl want to die? Apparently from the moment she set eyes on me she wanted to run her fingers through my hair.

'Hide me in your bedroom,' she persisted.*

'Unfortunately,' I had to tell her, 'I am sharing that with an elderly member of the staff.'

* *René Artois guarded his privacy intensely, but he was obviously no stranger to the Reds under the bed long before the Cold War had even begun.*

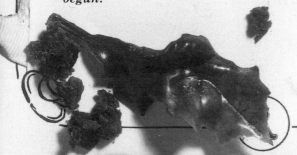

Tonight, for Edith, it was the big one.

'Ladies and gentlemen,' I announced, 'accompanied by sixty-four members of the New York Symphony Orchestra, conducted by Arturo Toscanini, Café Reńe is proud to present ... Madame Edith.'

My wife took centre stage. Monsieur Leclerc, hidden from the audience's view, wound up the gramophone. Unfortunately the old fool also knocked over the pile of records and lost his glasses. At last he signalled that all was well.

I tapped the bar with a spoon. 'Maestro – when you are ready.'

Leclerc sat at the piano, miming sixteen bars of a big piano concerto intro. Edith came in exactly on cue. The voice of Paul Robeson began to sing 'Ole Man River'.

'There is no doubt about it,' said Lieutenant Gruber, 'she is improving.'

Edith Artois does battle with the enemy ...

... and formally accepts Captain Bertorelli's unconditional surrender.

26 JULY

The sun is shining, the scent of summer is in the air. I should not have a care in the world. If I were not hiding two British airmen and two girls of the Communist Resistance and if I had not robbed a bank and stolen one million francs of Gestapo money and if Lieutenant Gruber did not think that I had something for him down my trousers, I probably wouldn't.

Michelle has microfilm of the German invasion plan. The RAF has sent a carrier bird that will fly it direct to London. I expected a carrier pigeon. Silly me. The RAF has of course provided us with a new long-distance duck. And she has given birth to a whole squadron of long-distance ducklings.

The effect on Yvette is not good. 'Oh look at those little babies,' she said. 'What does that make you think of?'

'Orange sauce and stuffing,' I said.

I shouldn't have mentioned the stuffing.

Yvette wants to run away to Paris with the money we stole from the bank. When I told her that the money was now down Lieutenant Gruber's trousers she burst into tears. I had to console her more or less immediately.

Edith arrived with a bowl of potato peelings.

'René! What are you doing with your arms around that girl?'

Stupid woman! Could she not see that Yvette was faint with hunger? That the young, innocent serving girl cried to see good food being given away to the ducks?

'Poor child,' Edith said. 'You must build your strength up. Here, have some potato peelings.'

Poems from the Front
of Hubert Gruber

I

I must go down to the café again,
To the lovely René in the square;
And all I ask is a little tank
And a joystick to drive me there.

I wandered lonely as a kraut
That floats in tanks o'er bumps and holes;
When all at once I saw a chap,
Mine host of golden wine and Bols;
Behind the bar in the back passage,
Would he like to give me a

Dear Uncle Heinrich,

Thank you for your letter of the 16th

With respect the Gestapo money that was stolen from the bank was not genuine. Yes of course it is the principle of the thing, but do not worry. I will detect the miscreants and bring them to justice — but not as you suggest. Uncle, you cannot expect me to shoot everybody in the town. I am unpopular enough already.

Your loving Nephew

Otto

P.S: By the way is there any chance of a postal order to tide me over

27 JULY

Himmler is very cross with Herr Flick about the missing Gestapo money. Helga thinks it must have been money from the Gestapo Christmas Club Fund. A lot of people will be going without their turkey and sinister trimmings this year if it isn't found.

She says Herr Flick is as mad as a snake because his his uncle is in a moody. He must get the money back quickly before there is an investigation and anybody starts asking questions about the paintings that were supposed to have been sent to Hitler. His plan is to disguise himself and Von Smallhausen as market traders, and try to catch a person spending one of the forged notes. The person will be arrested and interrogated until he leads them to the source. Seeing as I am the source, I am not altogether sure that this is a good plan.

28 JULY

Lieutenant Gruber wants to give the money anonymously to Herr Flick and put an end to the matter. The Colonel would rather not be hasty. After all, a million francs buys a lot of strudel.

29 JULY

Michelle appeared at the window tonight flicking a large chamois leather. My pulse quickened, but not for long. In her other hand was a bucket. It is her new cover. She has disguised herself as a window cleaner so that she can go from house to house without arousing suspicion. I think it will work better when she remembers to put some water in the bucket.

Anyway, she told me only once that she had the microfilm of the German invasion plans in a package. I am to attach it to the leg of the long-distance duck. The duck will transport it to London.

She produced the package. It was as big as a brick.

'For this you will need a long-distance albatross,' I protested.

Luckily the microfilm was only a tiny part of the package. Unluckily, there is a problem with the duck. She and her four little ducks are inseparable. If she is taken away from them she will not reach Calais before she gets post-natal depression.

NOUVION RESISTANCE

FROM UNDER THE DESK OF: *Michelle*

CERTAIN RESISTANCE MEMBERS HAVE HAD DIFFICULTY IDENTIFYING THEIR DESIGNATED TARGETS. THE FOLLOWING SILHOUETTES SHOULD HELP DIFFERENTIATE BETWEEN FRIEND AND FOE:

CARRIER PIGEON ONE OF OURS

LONG-DISTANCE DUCK, ONE OF OURS

CAPTAIN BERTORELLI ONE OF THEIRS

LIEUTENANT GRUBER'S LITTLE TANK — ONE OF THEM

READ THIS VERY CAREFULLY, I WROTE IT ONLY ONCE

There are, alas, few mementoes of Michelle of the Resistance. She wrote to the greatest hero in all France during the war years, but evidently only once. I expected something a trifle more intimate than this Resistance circular, but I reproduce it here anyway

1 AUGUST

Denise Laroque is hiding in a wardrobe in the passage outside the bedroom of my wife's mother. I have to be very careful or she grabs me as I go past. This morning I was not careful and she grabbed me by the ball s.*

'I knew you would come to me, passion of my life. Just the sight of your brave face has made me giddy.'

'It is probably the smell of the mothballs that I have just crushed under my feet.'

Denise tells me she wants to kill the woman I am living with, bury her in the garden and hide with me in the sewers of Paris, popping up from time to time to kill the hated enemy. I can hardly wait.

* *Ballisters.*

Louise of the Communist Resistance delivers a secret massage.

2 AUGUST

Louise is hiding in the next wardrobe along. This morning she grabbed my buns. I was very upset – they were my favourite crusty ones, and Yvette had buttered them specially. Louise told me she had been cooped up all night thinking of me.

'I am eating these buns so that I might build up my strength so that we may run away together,' she announced.

I do not think that two sardines and a bit of cress will get her very far, but who am I to argue with a staunch Communist with her finger on the trigger?

She wants to kill Denise, hide her body in a disused refrigerator and fly away to the Alps where we can drop rocks on the Germans.

'Unfortunately,' I told her, 'we use our disused refrigerator, but the moment it breaks down I will let you know.'

7 AUGUST

Monsieur Alfonse has been to the hairdresser's to have his moustache restyled. The pomade that they use is their own preparation made from badger-grease and rose-petal water. He also had his hair shampooed with an extract of hedgehog to give it body. This has its drawbacks. At the sound of a car hooter it clenches itself into a ball.

M · ALFONSE

UNDERTAKERS

'Twenty-four hour service'

Dear Mutti,

Herr Flick is a genius. We disguised ourselves as fish-sellers today in the hope of catching a French peasant spending forged money. Herr Flick dressed as a fisherman. For me, he provided the costume of a fish wife.

'This looks like a good pitch,' he said to me in the town square. Then he started to call, 'I have the winkles, I have the winkles alive alive-o.'
I did so want my disguise to be successful, so I joined him.
'I have the crabs,' I called. 'I have the crabs, alive alive-o.'
'Von Smallhausen,' Herr Flick explained, 'you will drive people away. You are not a good fish-seller.'
His words crushed me. 'I am sorry, Herr Flick. Just tell me what to do....'
'Conger,' he commanded me 'conger.'
''Ere we go, 'ere we go, 'ere we go,' I sang, ''ere we go, 'ere we go, 'ere we go.....'
He hit me with an eel. I just know life would be better if I were taller, Mutti.

Yours under the weather

Bobby Cedric Von Smallhausen

---

* Historians of the Nouvion campaign will be intrigued to know that Englebert was not in fact the name with which Von Smallhausen was christened. Mutti had much to answer for.

8 AUGUST

Monsieur Alfonse and his restyled moustache have been arrested by Herr Flick and Von Smallhausen. He passed a forged note at the winkle stall and was caught. He protested that he was innocent but, as Herr Flick said, if that was the case then why was his hair standing on end in fright when they shone a desk-light at him?

Michelle is to blame. She used one of the stolen notes at the hairdresser's and the ageing embalmer ended up with it in his change. All I can say is, he must have given the hairdresser an awfully big one in the first place.*

Michelle put up a weak defence. 'For weeks I have not had my hair done,' she said. 'As head of the Resistance I have a position to maintain.'

I'm surprised at her. I expect those who serve under me to be made of firmer stuff.

But she did have a plan. On the radio under the bed of my wife's mother she ordered from London two pairs of 15-denier stockings for herself and a packet of suicide pills for me. The quick ones.

* *Large denomination note.*

9 AUGUST

I don't think it was the mention of suicide pills that made me faint. I have been exerting myself more than usual in the kitchen recently, examining the melons and kneading the dumplings, and I think the effort has taken its toll. All the same, I'd like to know what Michelle has in mind.

10 AUGUST

The duck was ready for l unching.*

'Do you have the long-distance dick?' a policeman asked me as I carried the box into the square. 'I will mauve these peasants out of the wee and make a clear pith.'

'This will go down in history as the turning-point in the struggle of the oppressed people of the world against the jackboots of the fascist imperialists,' Edith said.

It was indeed an impressive moment. Tension mounted as she pulled open the trap. At last, the long-distance duck was free and she waddled out. Four little chicks were close behind. We chased the lot of them around the square but nothing got airborne. Eventually Mummy duck seemed to remember her training, and was last seen walking past the Post Office in the general direction of the coast. I hope she is careful. One German convoy and her family will be orphans.

---

* René has dwelt upon the melons and dumplings at some length, but I don't think he's planning to get his teeth into any other delicacies. The missing letter must be 'a'. The duck is ready for take-off.

14 AUGUST

The Communist girls have thrown Mimi out of her bedroom and forced her to sleep in the broom cupboard. I told her to look on the bright side – it is next to the hot-water tank so she'll be nice and warm.

'Blood of my life,' Denise Laroque said to me later in the privacy of her wardrobe, 'my heart pounds like a sea of passion crashing on the rocks of my desire. I have but to look at you and I see clouds scudding across the moon, trees bending on a tropical shore ...'

Mon Dieu, I cannot even swim.

15 AUGUST

'My passion is greater than her passion,' Louise tells me. 'Inside me surges a tidal wave of need that is waiting to crash upon the firm rocks of your manhood and to tumble us both into a whirlpool of ecstasy.'

I must remember to leave a rubber ring by my bed.

She wants me to dangle out of my window at midnight. She will dangle out of hers, and we'll meet on the parapet and make wild, abandoned love. It will certainly give the neighbours something to talk about.

She has gone now to do five hundred press-ups so that she will be able to go the distance. What is it about me that turns nice girls into hooligans? Can nobody resist?

16 AUGUST

I wish Lieutenant Gruber could.

He and the Colonel are worried that the missing money will be traced back to me. Well actually, they're worried that it will be traced back to me and then back to them. The Colonel has short-listed a choice of two plans.

The first is for Edith to make a pasty into which I will put a suicide pill. We will chuck it through the bars of Monsieur Alfonse's cell. He will gobble it up and that will be the end of it.

The other is for me to take the pill myself. But, as I said to Lieutenant Gruber, I am sure the undertaker will be happy to die for France.
And if I know Edith's pasties, we shouldn't need to waste a suicide pill.

Monsieur Alfonse cannot stand the torture.

17 AUGUST

Monsieur Alfonse has had a heart attack at Gestapo headquarters. Helga was alone with him when it happened, explaining to him that she wanted to help him escape because she also was in possession of some of the money and didn't want Herr Flick to find out. Monsieur Alfonse wanted proof that this was not just a Gestapo subterfuge. Helga opened her jacket and shirt to reveal a black lacy bra stuffed with big ones.*

But that wasn't the end of it. She also lifted her skirt to reveal a hacksaw blade, which happened to be concealed in the top of her black silk stocking, which happened to be attached to frilly black suspenders. The old boy's dicky ticker flicked at a quick lick, and he is now in the German wing of Nouvion General Hospital.

Well-wishers congratulate René Artois on his achievement of First Prize in the 1942 Nouvion Knockwurst Festival.

* *At least ten thousand francs' worth, by my estimation.*

19 AUGUST

Crabtree was wicking down the street when suddenly he licked at his watch and saw the tomb. Good groocious, he sod to himself, I should be spooking to my opposite nimber in London on the roodio. It was a quitter-past six.

He came into the café and I took him upstairs to the room of my wife's mother. His truncheon was swinging from his belt as we entered and the sight of it seemed to take Fanny back to the old days. She made a grab for it but Crabtree said he had new time to west.

' 'Allo, 'allo – secret agent Crabtree cooling,' he said. 'Connect me to Wombledon one-sox, one-sox.'

'Receiving you lewd and clore,' said the voice at the other end. 'Hold the loon, I will connoct you.'

My God. There was another one at the other end.

We eventually got through, but it was MacFisheries, and they were shut.

'Bigger,' said Crabtree. 'A wrong nimber. I will go and chock it in my address bike.'

It was at this moment that I spotted the mouth of my wife's mother wrapped around the pasty in which was the suicide pill. I at once drew Edith's attention to a few chores that needed doing at the other end of the room, but then she, too, saw the pasty and the game was up. The old bat had taken a bite but it came out intact. She hadn't had her teeth in.

20 AUGUST

Read this very carefully – I shall write it only once. Michelle of the Resistance has got a plan that involves fitting the bravest man in all France with a false bottom.

It is clear that we must get into the hospital to rescue Monsieur Alfonse before he talks. To do this she suggests that we disguise ourselves as ambulance workers, pushing a trolley with a concealed compartment. In it will be a dummy of Monsieur Alfonse wearing pyjamas. On top of the trolley will be a patient requiring emergency treatment. The idea is to exchange Monsieur Alfonse for the dummy. The emergency case will then demand a second opinion in another hospital and he will be pushed out.

I have volunteered to be the emergency case who lies on top of the rescued undertaker. I would do the same for anyone. With the possible exception of Lieutenant Gruber.

TEMPERATURE CHART

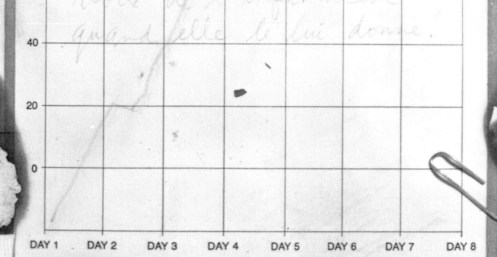

140

21 AUGUST

120 What a pity Michelle did not co-ordinate her plan with
Helga, who at that very moment was inventing an
exploding bedpan with which to eliminate Monsieur
100 Alfonse. It was to be activated by remote control.

'How do we know when the bedpan is in position?'
Lieutenant Gruber asked her.

'In it there is a microphone,' Helga barked. 'We can
80 hear the voice of the nurse when she gives it to him.'

60

40

20

0

DAY 1   DAY 2   DAY 3   DAY 4   DAY 5   DAY 6   DAY 7   DAY 8

N O U V I O N
G E N E R A L   H O S P I T A L

NAME: M. ALFONSE

TEMPERATURE CHART

140

120

100

22 AUGUST

We have arrived at the hospital. I was on the trolley and the dummy was under it. Another dummy was pushing it – Crabtree, dressed in a long surgeon's coat and mask, large, loose rubber gloves and a pair of rubber boots.

'It is a good disgeese,' he said. 'I can wick anywhere in the hospital without areesing sispoocion. All they can see is my eebrews.'

The bravest man in all France on his way to another secret operation.

DAY 8

NAME: M. ALFONSE

26 AUGUST

I still have not got over the shock. Not so much the trauma of the explosion, more the terrible sight of Lieutenant Gruber and the Colonel dressed as nurses. One of my fondest fantasies has been shattered.

The two Florence Nightingales appeared on the ward just as we were bundling Monsieur Alfonse under the trolley. Helga and Captain Bertorelli were outside, up against the hospital wall. Helga was bending over the radio set. Bertorelli was priming his plunger. Both were ready for a big bang.

'Bedpan to Control,' Gruber whispered into the container, 'Bedpan to Control.'

'Hello Bedpan,' Helga replied, 'we are ready to activate.'

Michelle, Edith and Crabtree disappeared off to retrieve the dummy from Monsieur Alfonse's room, leaving me alone on the trolley in a corridor. It wasn't long before a German soldier appeared. I whispered a hasty warning to Monsieur Alfonse, and in the panic his equipment began to bleep wildly. To allay suspicion I disguised the noise by whistling a tune. I chose the 'Ritual Fire Dance'. The soldier looked at me with a strange expression on his face, then finally walked on.

I breathed a sigh of relief, but the danger was not past. The idiot Crabtree had parked the trolley right outside the operating theatre. A German surgeon poked his head through the swing doors. He wore gloves and a gown, and a pair of the thickest pebble glasses I had ever seen.

'Where is the French peasant woman?' he asked, feeling his way along the wall. 'I am ready to perform the Caesarean.'

I will be in Lieutenant Gruber's eternal debt for finding Monsieur Alfonse's bed at that precise moment, positioning the badpan under it, and sending the signal for Bertorelli to press the plunger.

27 AUGUST

The explosion was the biggest I had heard since the night
Edith found me demonstrating to Yvette how to escape
from a German position. The surgeon scarpered for
shelter, and Monsieur Alfonse began to push me like the
clappers.

It is a quarter past one in the morning and I have just
crept into my café wearing a hospital gown after trudging
five miles from the Nouvion General Hospital where I was
in the maternity ward.

Am I really writing this? Maybe it is all a terrible
dream.

No, it is not. The draught blowing up the back of my
gown tells me it is true.

28 AUGUST

I had just put away my diary in the early hours of yesterday
morning when Lieutenant Gruber appeared at the café
door.

'Are you open?' he asked
'Partly,' I said, adjusting the gown.
The Lieutenant beamed.
'It is for the air-raids,' I said. 'One has to be ready to
leap in and out of one's clothes very quickly. But why are
you here at this hour, Lieutenant? Shouldn't you be in your
little tank, practising a few manoeuvres with Clarence?'

Gruber told me that Monsieur Alfonse had been
eliminated. So now we are all in the clear.

'Do you fancy a little something to celebrate?' he
offered.

I turned to go to the bar but suddenly thought better

of it. 'Er, not in the circumstances. I have to put the cat out.'

The Lieutenant was very persistent. He said he could put it out with me. He too has a little cat.

'Really? What is it?' I asked.

'A ginger tom.'

29 AUGUST

Yvette is full of apologies for driving off in the ambulance without me. Apparently they put Monsieur Alfonse in the back and thought I was with him.

'Did nobody stop to pick you up?' she asked.

'Yes,' I said. 'Three times. In the end I had to hide in the woods.'

Yvette had just begun to show her sympathy when Edith appeared with a burning candle in her hand.

'René! What are you doing with that girl?'

'Stupid woman, can you not see that she has been overcome by the anaesthetic on my operating gown?'

Edith apologised and told me to help Yvette upstairs. She would follow with the candle.

'Not while I'm wearing this gown,' I said. 'You help her upstairs and I will follow with the candle.'

30 AUGUST

Helga told me that Herr Flick suspects that the stolen money is hidden in Monsieur Alfonse's mortuary. He has despatched Von Smallhausen to gain entry and conduct a search. To do this without arousing suspicion, the miniature interrogator will be disguised as a corpse. I must warn Yvette to watch out for a little stiff.

31 AUGUST

Suddenly everyone wants to get rid of the money. And nobody wants to carry it.

Gruber thinks Helga should take it in her knickers.

'We cannot have Helga going through the town dropping notes of large denominations from her underwear,' said the Colonel. 'People would wonder what sort of army we are running.'

Gruber had another idea. 'If I may say so, Colonel – nobody would suspect that a man with feathers in his hat would have anything of great value down his trousers.'

'How-a you like a smack in the face, uh?' said the Italian.

The Colonel and Lieutenant Gruber convinced Bertorelli that he should bring the money to me in his trousers. This was a great pity. I didn't want it. It was hot money. And it would be even hotter after an hour or two in an Italian's southern region.

1 SEPTEMBER

There is a dark side to the Colonel that I never suspected.

He has ordered Helga to keep the Italian under close observation. The moment he departs for the café she is to inform him. The Colonel is going to snitch to the Gestapo, who will have him arrested. In one stroke the money will be returned and the Colonel will be rid of the irritating wop.

2 SEPTEMBER

Crabtree has a message for me. It seems that Michelle is in the town square with a new escoop apparootis for the British earmin.

'When I give her the secret sognal she will appear like a phantom out of the newt,' he said.

Some secret. He went to the door and gave a long, loud blast on his whistle.

'Listen very carefully,' Michelle said as she slipped up the back passage. 'I shall say this only once. The Germans are about to put into action a new and terrible secret weapon.'

I was tempted to say that if it was as secret as Crabtree's signal it would be all over Europe by Tuesday.

'It is a very big bum,' said Crabtree.

Apparently it is a new type of landmine, a development of the Mark Five. The Mark Sox, according to Crabtree. The Resistance has captured two of them and hollowed them out. As the police interpreter explained, Michelle's plin is to ploce the two British earmin inside. The bums will be loaded on a bummer on a dick night, and they will be dripped over Ongland.

It occurred to me that this might well kill them, but apparently that has been thought of. The earmin will wear parashats.

'The lods of the bums will be secured by stell nits. Each earmin will have a spinner. As they descond they will unscrew their nits,' Crabtree continued.

Well, it will be one way of pissing the time.

'Then they will remauve the lod and immediately jump and open their parashats,' he concluded.

Frankly I want no part in this crazy plan. I am resigning from the Resistance.*

* One of René's little jokes.

Dear Mumsy,

        I say old thing,
I've been thinking about this new escape
plan. I'm a bit windy about it. For
instance, how do we find our nuts in
the dark? Carstairs and I have
been looking into this frightfully
carefully in the last few days.
    We've decided to cover them with
    luminous paint
        Yours in a tizz,

           Fairfax

My mother is surprised to see that her memories of René don't hold a candle to Mimi's.

5 SEPTEMBER

Mimi wants to know when these girls of the Communist Resistance are going to leave us. She wants her room back so that we can fly away together on a magic gossamer cloud of happiness and enchantment. I have a shrewd suspicion she is talking about her duvet.

Oh Mimi – so much passion bottled up in such a small container.

6 SEPTEMBER

Great news for all those girls wanting to fly away with their bosses on a magic gossamer cloud of happiness and enchantment: the girls of the Communist Resistance have held a branch meeting and by a democratic vote of twelve to three they are moving to Abbeville.

'If I should die your name will be found carved on my heart,' Denise told me.

That's nice, as long as she doesn't put my address on as well.

As for Louise, she said that as soon as it is safe she will kill Denise and come back and take what is hers.

'What have you left behind?' I asked helpfully.

'You. I make you a solemn promise that you will be kidnapped, bound hand and foot, and brought to me within a month.'

'I'm a little tied up as it is,' I replied.

7 SEPTEMBER

The Colonel was very eager to snitch on Captain Bertorelli this morning but Herr Flick wasn't answering his phone. Typical secret police; never there when you need them.

All the Colonel could get was his answering machine. 'This is a recorded Gestapo message,' said the voice. 'I am not taking calls at the moment but you may leave a message on the revolving wax disc. Please speak after the gunshot.'

Pretending to be an anonymous French peasant, the Colonel left the tip-off that the stolen money was in the trousers of a man with feathers in his hat who could be found at Café René.

'I would tell you more,' the Colonel said, 'but my money is running out. Pip, pip, pip, pip.'

I'm tired. Must remember to give Yvette a note about the shopping.

The old pillow-stuffer looks like having his feathers ruffled.

8 SEPTEMBER

Woke up to find that Yvette had given me one.

Dear, romantic child. She does not realise the candlesticks are only electro-plated. She will be heartbroken. It was certainly a shock to me when I took them to the pawnbroker's.

I had just finished reading when the Itie Bertorelli arrived at the café. He went straight over to Edith.

'I have-a for you a lot of something which once-a René had but no longer he got,' he whispered.

Feathers?

He said he want-a to take her upstairs, take-a his trousers down and-a give her one million francs.

I wasn't convinced that this was a fair rate of exchange, so to save him the stairs, I took the money myself. Mimi hid it in the oven.

Moments later Lieutenant Gruber arrived and told me the Gestapo would be arriving any minute to arrest the man with the feathers in his hat who had the stolen money in his trousers.

A minute later Leclerc arrived, disguised as an old pillow-stuffer. He was indistinguishable from the genuine article, as usual. In the pillows were parachutes for the airmen. In his hat were the feathers.

Herr Flick was seconds behind him. He was wearing his sinister black overcoat and an expression that said, 'I am as mad as a snake.' He had received information that the man with feathers in his hat had down his trousers something of interest to the Gestapo.

'It is I, Leclerc,' the old fool pleaded with me.

'I have never seen you before in my life,' I said.*

It is many years since I sat down alone, rolled up my sleeves, and let my hands glide up and down the old instrument. So many years, in fact, that at first I thought perhaps I wouldn't remember how. But the moment my fingers started their rhythmic caress, it all came back to me.

Attracted by the sound of my efforts, Edith crept into the room and slipped her arm around me.

'You had a strong left hand in the old days,' she said with a glint in her eye, 'and the fingers of your right hand seemed to be everywhere.'

It is true. There was not a note that was safe. I played in all the bars those days. I was known as Syncopated Sydney. For all I know, in some bars, I still am.

* *It may have been after this incident that René drew up the notice I reproduce here. It was placed behind the bar at the Café René:*

NOT WANTED!

AT ANY PRICE!

THIS MAN IS A MASTER OF DISGUISE AND SHOULD BE AVOIDED WHENEVER POSSIBLE. ON **NO** ACCOUNT SERVE HIM ALCOHOLIC LIQUOR!

THE OLD PILLOW-STUFFER

THE OLD KNOCKWURST PURVEYOR

THE OLD CHEESE-SELLER

THE OLD FORGER

THE OLD PUTTY-SELLER

THE OLD MOUNTAINEER

THE OLD SPANISH ACCORDION-PLAYER

THE OLD PIANO-PLAYER

THE SILLY OLD FOOL

THE OLD COBBLER

Ⓡ

The reason that I was once again tickling the ivories was sad but simple. Monsieur Leclerc has been arrested by the Gestapo because Berlin suspects he has something of great value down his trousers. I can only think that this rumour was started by my wife's mother.

'Do you remember how I sang to you under the old willow tree by the river?' Edith asked.

How could I forget? As I played and she began to sing, it all came flooding back.

'Yes,' I sighed. 'The trouble I had lugging the piano down there.'

The emotion of the occasion was too much for Edith.

'Oh René,' she purred, 'let us get married again! What have we got to lose?'

'Nothing we have not lost already,' I said.

'Are you afraid that I might be unfaithful to you and run off with a younger man? René, I am in the autumn of my life. There is the hammer-toe on my right foot, the bunion on my left, the first murmurings of sciatica in my right hip ...'

'You might still hobble off with a younger man.'

Edith promised that from now on she will be by my side twenty-four hours a day. I thought immediately of one or two times and places when that might be a little inconvenient, but I didn't have the heart to tell her.*

'Edith, I do not know a man who could resist such an offer, but you forget Denise Laroque. She is wild about me. She would shoot any woman whose lips even brushed against mine.'

'Oh René, you are my wonder man. Always you think only of me. Just let me kiss those magic fingers.'

I told her it was not safe. One of Denise's friends might have seen us through the window. I made her pull my hand down behind the piano and do her nibbling there.

* René is so considerate of his wife's feelings. It was man's work in the cupboard under the stairs. And it goes without saying that he wouldn't have wanted his dear wife to be present while he was lifting tenderloins in the larder or humping in the coal cellar.

12 SEPTEMBER

There was a terrible smell wafting around the café this morning. It was too early for Lieutenant Gruber to have been in wearing that special aftershave of his – lily-of-the-valley with a hint of diesel oil – and, as far as I knew, my wife's mother was up in her room.

No, she wasn't. She had decided to cook herself a big baked potato, the one I had concealed behind the cistern in the bathroom – the one that contained the spy camera for photographing the German invasion plans.

She was baking it in the oven.

Thanks to the stupid old interfering bat, the best part of the hidden one million francs had gone up in smoke.

It wasn't so much the money that I cared about. I knew it was forged. But I wasn't going to take the blame for the camera.

'I shall tell the Resistance that it was your fault, you deaf old crone,' I said.

'Then I will tell the Germans about the paintings, the airmen, the stolen landmines,' she snarled. 'I can finger you buddy and get you sent to the big house just like that . . .'

She snapped her fingers to emphasise the point.

I decided to give her the poison pasty treatment again on the first day she remembers to put her teeth in.

13 SEPTEMBER

Good moaning. Guess who had bad nose for me this morning?

A poster has been pisted on the wills of the Town Squeer. It is a picture of Roger Leclerc without his trousers. It reads: 'Unless the money stolen from the Gestapo is returned within twenty-four hours this man will be shot in the Town Square.'

There are worse places to be shot, as I know to my cost. Leclerc may find this small consolation of course, but what can we do?

We cannot give back the money; it is so hot it's cremated. We cannot forge some more; the forger is the one they are going to shoot. Time is of the essence. Every minute counts. We must act at once.

14 SEPTEMBER

There again, if he is not here to play the piano, then Edith will not be able to sing.

15 SEPTEMBER

But on the other hand, under threat of death he may reveal our connections with the Resistance and we could all be shot in the Town Square.

I know Leclerc. He is a brave man. He will hold out until the very last minute, bravely hoping that the money will be returned.

And when it is not? He will drop us in it.

CAFÉ RENÉ

Lieutenant Gruber enquired after my health tonight. I looked pale, he said, and my hands were trembling.

'It is the worry of the war, you know,' I said to him. 'Hoping that you are going to win.'

Gruber told me he had come to help me to give the money back to the Gestapo so that the pianist could be set free.

I told him about my wife's mother, the baked potato and the money that was now in ashes.

'This is not good news, René. But I could very likely help you if you could just let something else drop.'

Lieutenant Gruber has a gift for seeing things from a different and often surprising angle. I put it down to his artistic leanings.

'On the other hand,' I said, 'he was not a very good pianist.'

I could see that the Lieutenant had more on his mind than the fate of geriatric piano-players. At length he came out with it.

'René, do you have any information that may lead to the return of the missing landmines? If they were returned I am sure I could arrange the release of the pianist. Remember, René, my door is always open.'

I didn't doubt it.

My wife's mother is determined to rescue her lover, Roger Leclerc. She stole a handgrenade from the Germans and was setting off to storm Gestapo headquarters in her bathchair when Edith intercepted her.

'I will pull out the pin with my teeth,' the old bat spat, 'and stick it through their letter-box.'

Unfortunately she'd left her teeth by the bedside and Edith managed to talk her out of it.

It's a great pity, she would have died a glorious death.

Fanny finally locates her spare set of teeth.

18 SEPTEMBER

For Monsieur Leclerc, I fear, the war will very soon be over.

Herr Flick has orders from Berlin requiring the Colonel to provide a firing squad to execute the wandering pillow-stuffer. The order was signed by Heinrich Himmler in person.

'I keep-a this,' said Captain Bertorelli when he was shown the piece of paper. 'Me, I collect-a the autographs.'

It seems that because Lieutenant Gruber ran the last firing squad, it's the Italian's turn this time. Bertorelli's men will pull their triggers at seven o'clock tomorrow, and Leclerc will have played his very Last Waltz.

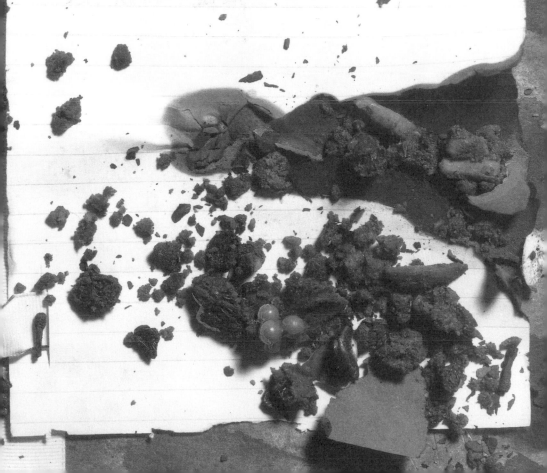

19 SEPTEMBER

It was ten minutes to seven and there was no sign of Leclerc.

Michelle had instructed the RAF to drop the money to us last night. Crabtree wetted all night in the woods flushing his titch. The bummers pissed overhead but the clods were very loo and it was a bit figgy.

Then it was five to seven and there was every sign of Monsieur Leclerc. He had been marched into the square and put against the wall.

'If the money is not returned in two minutes the wandering pillow-stuffer will die,' hissed Herr Flick. His words echoed off the stone walls and shopfronts of downtown Nouvion.

One minute to seven. I felt so sorry for the old boy. Even if the Italians missed, Michelle had guns trained on him by her markswomen in case he cracked at the last minute and dropped us in it. If the RAF were late, she didn't want to take any chances.

The church bell began to toll. At the seventh stroke, with the tension so electric that even the feathers on Captain Bertorelli's hat stood on end, the air was shattered by a long, loud droning noise that grew and grew in intensity.

Had Leclerc's nerve finally cracked? No. My eyes were drawn to something fluttering in the breeze. Banknotes. Thousands of them. The RAF had arrived at last, and money rained down from a squadron of bombers. One million French francs – minus, of course, the small commission deducted by the Nouvion Chamber of Commerce for services rendered.

As one uniformed bystander so rightly remarked: 'Just in the nick of tomb.'

20 SEPTEMBER

'What do you fancy this time?' I asked Yvette in the cellar
tonight. 'Smooth and velvety, or for a change maybe, a
bit of the rough stuff?'

'Oh René,' she said, her fingers tight around one of my
tumblers as I reached for the jugs. 'You make it so hard
for me. I will love whatever pleases you, so long as it makes
my heart sing and my knees tremble.'

Tasting the local vintages so that I may choose a house
wine for my café is indeed a difficult task. Some wines
tonight were too good for the peasants. Others were simply
too bad for them, though good enough for the Germans.

At last I got my hands on something firm and full-
bodied.

'Put another pint of anti-freeze in each barrel,' I told
Yvette. 'And then you can come and help me with the
laying down.'

Crabtree in the dark.

21 SEPTEMBER

Not altogether to my surprise, I awoke this morning with an enormous smile on my face.

A great load has been lifted from my shoulders. The Gestapo have received back their money, Leclerc is free and they are no longer searching for Monsieur Alfonse. All I need now is for my wife's mother to spontaneously combust and I'll have the grand slam. But for the moment we are free to make as much money out of the war as we can.

'René!' Yvette called. 'Michelle wants you in the back room.'

Oh heck. I knew it could not last.

Michelle was always proud of her big berets.

22 SEPTEMBER

Michelle was wearing dirty dungarees and a false moustache, and was carrying a brick menacingly in each hand. The very sight of them made my eyes water.

It is her new disguise. She is a builder.

'If the Germans find me here,' she said, 'I am repairing your window.'

'But it is not broken,' I said.

Very carefully and only once, Michelle chucked one of the bricks through a pane.

'It is now,' she said.

She brought bad news. 'When we stole from the Germans the landmines in which the British airmen are going to escape we had to remove one thousand kilos of high explosive. You are probably wondering what happened to the explosive.'

'To tell you the truth,' I said, 'I never gave it a thought.'

She went on regardless. The explosive was hidden in a pudding factory, she said, and the Resistance had secret information that this factory was to be commandeered by the Germans for the manufacture of frozen strudel which was to be sent in food parcels to the Russian Front. Naturally the Resistance could not leave this explosive to fall into German hands. And – surprise, surprise – they have therefore arranged for it to be delivered to my café.

All one thousand kilos will be disguised as a product of the factory. To wit, five hundred Christmas puddings.

Are these people out of their minds?

I told Michelle I wanted nothing to do with her puddings, and that was final.*

---

* *This is not like René. Usually he would have been the first to volunteer his help with Michelle's puddings. Perhaps he had a headache.*

23 SEPTEMBER

Michelle went away sulking. Soon afterwards she sent through my window a coded hate letter. It was wrapped around her unused brick.

'What is the matter with you?' I finally deciphered. 'All you have to do is sit in your comfortable café and hide a few paltry Christmas puddings. How would you like to be a twenty-four-hour emergency plumber with putty under your finger nails, burning your hands on the blow lamp, drinking tea from a paint kettle and sitting down on a pile of bricks to eat a doorstep sandwich with a twelve-inch spanner in your back pocket?'

I'm sorry to say I softened at this point. But I wasn't half as sorry as Yvette.*

24 SEPTEMBER

Would you believe that I have received a bill for repairs to a broken window?

25 SEPTEMBER

Two broken windows?

---

* *I had not previously realised the depth of my mother's feelings for Michelle.*

26 SEPTEMBER

Lieutenant Gruber was rather in his cups today.

'I think the Colonel and I were not cut out for the military life,' he confided sadly. 'Every night the Colonel prays that Hitler will not invade England. That damned English weather will be fatal for his rheumatism. And the food! Before the war I was one month in a small hotel in Croydon. Do you know, René, they eat faggots for breakfast?'

I imagine he left Croydon in rather a hurry.

27 SEPTEMBER

The Lieutenant is a mine of information in his present mood. General Von Klinkerhoffen told him that it has come to the ears of Hitler that two of the new Mark Six landmines are missing from this district. Hitler has of course flown into one of his familiar rages.

'Has he eaten the carpet?' Gruber asked the General.

'He has done a lot of no good to a reproduction of the Bayeux tapestry.'

'Do you think he has a screw loose?'

'It is my opinion that a whole Meccano set has fallen apart in there.'

Dear Mutti,

Herr Flick is so beastly to

Yesterday he was on the telephone. 'Yes mein Führer,' he was saying, 'no, mein Führer, of course, mein Führer. I understand, mein Führer. I am very grateful to you, mein Führer. Goodbye, mein Führer.'

'Was that the Führer?' I asked him.

'No it was my mother.' She was checking to see if my underwear which she has knitted for me is a snug fit.'

'And is it?'

'Mind your business.'

This is typical of how he snaps at me. Its so unfair. I try my best. What more can a man of five foot two do?'

Your loving overgrown fruitbat

Bobby Cedric Von Smallhausen

P.S: Thank you for me stacked heels. Unfortunately Herr Flick noticed that I was six inches taller and ridiculed me without mercy. I now use them as bookends for my collection of Trenchcoat Monthly.

Monsieur Alfonse offers Fanny a special deal.

29 SEPTEMBER

Monsieur Alfonse has delivered to my café fifty-eight exploding Christmas puddings concealed in a coffin.

My wife's mother took one look at it and went screaming back upstairs as fast as she could hobble.

'It's an ill wind,' she shrieked to nobody in particular.

'We'd better open the windows,' I said.

Dear Mutti,
    Berlin expects the Gestapo to find the missing
landmines, We are just the boys for the job, I tell
Herr Flick. It is his opinion that much of the
subversive activity in Nouvion is conducted at
René's café.
    'Gestapo spies tell me that there are frequent
comings and goings in the larder,' he said to me.
    'I do not remember mentioning this,' I said.
    'You are not the only sneaky pebble on the beach,'
he snapped.
    He produced a map. 'We must find the position
from which we can observe these things. I have
decided upon the church tower. From there we can
see directly into the larder and the upstairs
windows.'
    You know how much I have always wanted
to look down on the Resistance. I realised now
was my big chance.
    'Herr Flick, you are a marvel,' I said. 'You will
go a long way with your brain.'
    'And you will go nowhere with yours,' he said.

Your son,
    Bobby Cedric Von Smallhausen

30 SEPTEMBER

Helga tells me that Herr Flick and Von Smallhausen have removed their clothes in order to follow the Führer's instructions. They have disguised themselves so that they can merge into an ecclesiastical background.

Herr Flick is dressed as a monk, complete with open-toed sandals that he made himself. Von Smallhausen is similarly dressed, but with a halo hanging over his head. It was part of the set.

Herr Flick has ordered Helga to bring to the church tower, at four o'clock, coffee and sandwiches to sustain them during their vigil.

'What will you be doing in the church tower?' she asked.

'Snooping.'

Helga finds the lengths to which Herr Flick will go to achieve his ends very exciting. She wanted to kiss him, but unfortunately the rules of the order to which he belongs forbid any physical contact with girls.

1 OCTOBER

Crabtree arrived this afternoon with two expleeding Christmas poddings.

'I suppose they are down your trousers as usual?' I asked wearily.

'Do not be redoculous,' he said, throwing aside his cape to reveal a lovely pair of puddings slung around his neck. 'Do not drip them or they may go off bong.'

'How do I account for the very obvious presence of sixty Christmas puddings in the larder in September?' I asked Yvette as we were struggling to get our legs over them.

'Say we are members of a pudding club,' she suggested.

The girl from the hat shop with the big berets announces that she is in the club.

2 OCTOBER

Edith said there was a girl outside who wanted to see me. She told my wife it was a private matter.

'I am glad you are open,' she said as she came in. She was wearing a raincoat, under which she appeared to be wearing a very large bump. She pointed at it. 'I did not want to leave this on your doorstep.'

'I deny ever having seen this girl before,' I said.

'I am not the only one,' she said. 'Six more girls are outside.'

I hesitated.

'We are in the club,' she said.

This was going to take some explaining.

The six girls came in, all with big bumps.

'And there is a busload coming at seven o'clock,' said one of them.

I was calculating my chances of making it to the door without being scythed in half by Edith's kitchen knife when one of the girls threw open her coat.

'One exploding pudding,' she said proudly.

Phew! I felt like all my Christmases had come at once.

René casts an anxious eye over my mother's explosive puddings.

Dear Mumsy,
                        all tickety-boo here.
What's up your end? I really think I'm
  getting the hang of this landmine
business, although after six hours cooped
up in one, the upper leg is as stiff as
the upper lip.
        Tonight the girls from the Resistance
are going to screw us in the landmines
and then drop them. It sounds like
a jolly difficult way of going about
things, but there you are.
        With any luck the bombers will
head over Wimbledon. I could hail
a cab and be home for supper.
        First, though, we're going to hide out
again in the Froggy café-owner's
        cellar.
            Toodle-pip,
            Your son,
            Fairfax

3 OCTOBER

Brother Otto has had a mishap in the church tower. A rising rope caught him unawares and now he is suspended by the clappers.

Brother Englebert is not much better off. One of the church bells has fallen and completely enveloped him.

Dear Mutti

Sorry if the writing is wobbly but it's very dark in here. A bell fell on my head an hour ago.

I know it was an hour ago because I just heard Herr Flick say so. A tiny gap has opened up between the bell and the floorboards of the church tower. I think perhaps Herr Flick is starting to winch up the bell to save me. Maybe he values me after all.

'I would have expected some whimpering noise by now,' I heard him say to Helga.

Whimper, Mutti? Me? The long distance limping champion of Westphalia three years running?

'There is not much room for air to be admitted through the small crack,' I heard Helga reply. 'Perhaps he has suffocated.'

'I see his hand protruding,' said Herr Flick. 'Tread on it.'

Helga did so.

'Aaaagh! I responded.

They started to ask me questions. I was to bong once for yes, and twice for no.

'Do you wish to have a ham sandwich?' Helga shouted.

I bonged once.

'With mustard?'

I bonged twice.

'Hold the mustard.'

Through the crack came one end of a thick ham sandwich. Then it got stuck.

'Herr Flick,' Helga boomed, 'the sandwich is too thick.'
'Then remove the ham.'
She did so.
  I took the plain bread and sucked on it gratefully.
Half an hour later, in a supreme feat of strength,
Herr Flick lifted the bell clear. But instead of the
rapturous reunion I had had in mind, my superior
announced that he had bad news for me.
  'You have been squashed well below the minimum
height required for members of the Gestapo,'
he said. 'Let me have your resignation in the
morning.'

      I'm very upset now, so I'll write again
shortly.

        Bobby Cedric Von Smallhausen

10 OCTOBER

It is midnight, and a terrible disaster had occurred. The British airmen are still concealed in empty beer barrels in my cellar instead of being airborne somewhere over England, waiting to be dropped from a German bomber. Herr Flick and his assistant Von Smallhausen are in the Heinkel instead.

It seems that while he was suspended by the clappers in the church tower Herr Flick saw something suspicious in the builder's yard next to the café. According to Helga he and Von Smallhausen went to investigate, found the landmines, and decided to occupy them.

It was Herr Flick's opinion that under cover of darkness the Resistance would transport the mines to their secret headquarters. As soon as they heard somebody speaking in the French language, they would leap out, subdue them, arrest them and march them to Gestapo headquarters. Frankly I think they are as mad as hatters but that is the Gestapo for you.

But I disgress. The Colonel also located the mines, thanks to Lieutenant Gruber maintaining his position at my café.

He got Bertorelli's men to load them on to a truck and take them to the Luftwaffe base, not realising that they were stuffed full of men in sinister leather coats.

Michelle discovered that the mines had been moved.

'Do not worry,' she said, 'I have a plan.'

I started to worry.

'We have an agent at the base. We know precisely the position of the landmines. They are in the landmine stores. The barrels with the British airmen inside them will be taken to the air force base. They will be allowed in as a consignment of beer for the Sergeants' mess which is being sent with your compliments. Once past the guard, it will be a simple matter to get them into the landmine store because it is next to the Sergeants' mess.'

'I have to hand it to you, Michelle,' I said. 'You've come up with some ridiculous plans in your time, but you and your girls are very, very brave to do this.'   'Women are not allowed in at the base. You are going with Leclerc.'

We loaded the barrels containing the two British idiots on to barrows and set off for the base. The third British idiot led the way.

'Halt!' shouted the guard at the gate. 'What is the password?'

'On these two trilleys we have two borrels of boor for the Sergeants' miss,' said Crabtree as fluently as ever. 'They are a goft from Roné's Cifé. If you rood this handwroten nute all will be exploned.'

'What is he talking about?' the guard asked me.

'He is from the mountains,' I explained. 'This is a present of beer for the Sergeants' mess.'

'Pass, friend,' was the immediate reply.

Leclerc, Crabtree and I stole into the landmine store. I wanted us to find out quickly which were the empty landmines, get the airmen into them, and clear out of there like bats out of hell.

'I have a hammer,' said Leclerc. 'I will hit the casings and we will find out which ones are hollow.'

I stopped him just in time. There is definitely something wrong with that dithering old fool. The lights might be on, but there's nobody home.

Crabtree located the landmines – the empty ones with crosses on them. We were just about to pull off the lids when we heard the sound of boots on concrete. We hid. Two Germans arrived in service overalls, pushing barrows. Into each barrow they put one of the landmines.

'Dimnation,' whispered Crabtree. 'Footed at the eleventh ear.'

With heavy hearts, and heavier wheelbarrows, we headed for home.

My mother attempts to satisfy the appetites of the British airmen.

11 OCTOBER

I am not normally a drinking man, especially at half past eight in the morning, but my nerves are shot to pieces. I feel like a cat that has used eight of his nine lives. Why am I in this state? Firstly, I have a cellar full of 258 exploding Christmas puddings. Secondly, the British airmen, who were supposed to leave last night, are back following yet another British Intelligence cock-up.

Between you and me if there was enough money in the till I would leg it over the border with Yvette and start fighting my war in a different theatre. Since she is twenty years younger than me it might be an operating theatre but it's a risk I've had to come to terms with.

I still have the painting of the Fallen Madonna with the Big Boobies by Van Clomp together with the painting of the Cracked Vase with the Big Daisies by Van Gogh with which to finance our undercover activities, but could I leave my possessions? My café? My friends? My wife?

We heroes of the Resistance sometimes have to make these sacrifices.

12 OCTOBER

Michelle informs me that London has come up with a bold
and daring plan to get the British airmen back to England.

'I see,' I said. 'What hare-brained scheme are they
suggesting this time? Are they sending a submarine up
the canal at midnight?'

'It was supposed to be a secret.'

I do not believe it.

13 OCTOBER

I still do not believe it.

Perhaps I should not have underestimated the brilliance of the British Navy. The brave sailors are bringing a midget two-man submarine.

I can't help wondering: how do you fit four men into a two-man submarine?

Dear Mumsy,

I say it's all go.

Carstairs and I have just been measured for diving helmets. The jolly matelots are coming to get us; we're coming home astride a midget sub. Come and wave us in at Dover If it's a nice day, won't you?

The plan is for the Froggy café-owner to take us to the canal disguised as eel-fishers. He is a member of the Nouvion Fishing Club and apparently you fish for eels at night. Under cover of darkness he will row us and the diving helmets to the RV where we will meet the good old RN.

Goodness knows what'll happen If the Germans find us with two diving helmets. Perhaps the Froggy will say that the eels aren't biting and that we are going down to make sure that the bait is still on the hooks.

Anyway, must dash — It's all around the Resistance that Carstairs and I are pretty damned good divers, and for some reason the girls suddenly seem dashed eager to get us down into the cellar....

Shiver me timbers!

Your son, Fairfax.

17 OCTOBER

I was with Yvette in the back room when I told her I could no longer take the strain.

She was open mouthed.

'We will take the paintings,' I said. 'We will head for Switzerland and hide out in the mountains until the war is over. Nobody must suspect a thing. From now on we will not even talk to each other. When I am ready I will leave you a note telling you the time of the train.'

Silently, we had one last embrace.*

---

* *My mother confirms René's earlier claim that heroes of the Resistance would often do this, particularly at times of great tension. All these years later I still find it strangely touching.*

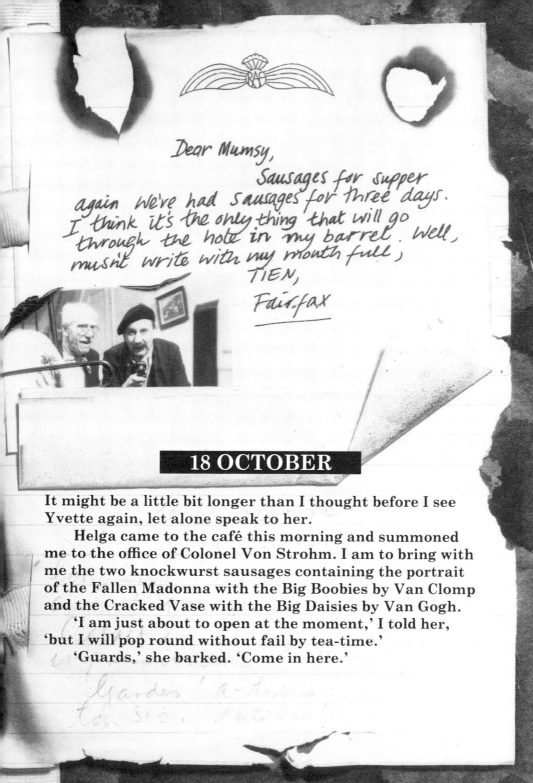

Dear Mumsy,
             Sausages for supper
again We've had sausages for three days.
I think it's the only thing that will go
through the hole in my barrel. Well,
musn't write with my mouth full,
                    TIEN,
                       Fairfax

18 OCTOBER

It might be a little bit longer than I thought before I see
Yvette again, let alone speak to her.

Helga came to the café this morning and summoned
me to the office of Colonel Von Strohm. I am to bring with
me the two knockwurst sausages containing the portrait
of the Fallen Madonna with the Big Boobies by Van Clomp
and the Cracked Vase with the Big Daisies by Van Gogh.

'I am just about to open at the moment,' I told her,
'but I will pop round without fail by tea-time.'

'Guards,' she barked. 'Come in here.'

12 NOVEMBER

Let me try to explain why it is several weeks since I last
made an entry and why I am now sitting in the toilet of
the 11.15 express to Geneva with a pile of paper in my hand.

It is a long story, the paper is French Railways
economy size and in short supply, and another passenger
is banging urgently on the door. So I will be as brief as I
can.

It turned out that the Colonel wanted the paintings
back because the General wanted to send them to Berlin
because Hitler wanted to give Eva Braun one. I offered him
the forgeries, but it seemed the Führer was taking no
chances: he was sending an art expert to authenticate the
paintings. But there was worse to come. The General had
demanded that the Colonel shoot the peasant who had been
hiding them.

'Do not worry, René,' the Colonel said. 'We have
known you for a very long time. We all feel very close to
you. We have decided to allow you to escape.'

'Oh thank you, Colonel,' I said. A couple of days to tie
up a few loose ends at the café and say goodbye to old
friends, and I'd comfortably catch the Weekend Saver to
Zurich.

'We will give you sixty seconds start, commencing now. Go.'

I went.

Unbeknown to any of us at the time, however, Herr Flick had been informed by his godfather Heinrich Himmler that Hitler could not have telephoned General Von Klinkerhoffen because for the last week he had been shacked up in a tent deep in the Black Forest having the secret nookie with Eva Braun. I always thought Hitler was above that sort of thing, but it seems he is crumpet-mad.

Herr Flick told Helga and Von Smallhausen that he planned for them to recover the paintings while in transit by train to Berlin.

'We will sell them and then we will run away to a tropical island,' he said. 'There we will lead a simple life together dressed in banana leaves as we frolic in the surf under the warm sun. Does this appeal to you?'*

A I L W A Y   P R O P E R

* As things turned out, there was a last-minute change of plan. Suddenly in late 1945 they decided to honeymoon on the upper reaches of the Amazon Basin, and I'm told that they were so taken by the natives that they decided to make their home there.

Herr Flick ordered Helga to sell their canvases of The Fallen Madonna with the Big Boobies and The Cracked Vase with the Big Daisies and they opened a small cinema, The Flick House, on the proceeds. If they had had possession of the originals it would have been a large cinema.

I hear that to this day they play re-runs of old Erich von Stroheim movies to packed audiences. Helga shines her torch into the customers' eyes and instructs them to buy ices and soft drinks, whilst Herr Flick spends much time in the projection room, operating the machinery. Von Smallhausen appears during the intervals, playing a small organ. Sometimes, carried away by the applause, he overstays his welcome and gets beaten over the head with a large knockwurst by the front-of-house manager.

'All except the sea,' said Von Smallhausen. 'I am not a very good swimmer.'

The Swedish art expert, Yup Von Hoop De Hoop, did indeed verify the authenticity of the two paintings.

'My client will be most satisfied,' he said to General Von Klinkerhoffen as he handed the German one million marks in the form of twenty gold bars.

'I will take the paintings personally to Geneva,' said Von Hoop De Hoop. 'The night express has in its guard's van a safe. My destination and mission is known only to you and to my client. I don't think that we have anything to worry about.'

Experience has taught me never to think ...†

---

† *It is not clear at this point whether René had run out of paper or if he realised that the other passenger's need was greater than his own.*

13 NOVEMBER

Little did Von Hoop De Hoop know that Helga was behind the curtains and had heard everything.

Me, I was on my way to the police station. So, minutes later, was General Von Klinkerhoffen. In fact I had only just arrived when I had to dive under the counter to escape discovery.

'Heil Hitler,' he said to the policeman on duty at the desk.

'Hole Hotler,' came the reply.

The General said he wanted to store some not very important papers in the police safe. His own safe at the château had been blown up by the Resistance. He sent the policeman from the room while he opened his briefcase to effect the transfer. I watched astonished as he pulled out twenty bars of gold.

'If you tell anyone about this you will be shot,' he told the policeman when Crabtree returned to the room.

'My lips are soiled,' was the reply.

The General left and Crabtree was called away with his lidder to roscue a Siamese pissy up a tree. I opened the safe with a spare key I found and helped myself to four gold bars.*

Back at the café, I scribbled a hasty note to Yvette.

'I have nicked a fortune in gold. We must leave tonight for the mountains. Be on the 11.15 Geneva Express. Here is the ticket for the sleeper. Your own René.'

I put it in a buff envelope and gave it to Leclerc to give secretly to Yvette.

Then I wrote Edith a tender note to say goodbye.

'Goodbye,' the note said.

---

* *René again worries about how to finance his war effort.*

Madame X prepares
herself for action.

14 NOVEMBER

Then I added: 'It is best for both of us that I leave you. Do
not grieve for me. Monsieur Alfonse will make you a fine
husband. Yours faithfully, René Artois.'

I put it in a white envelope and gave it to Leclerc. I
said I hoped he wouldn't mix them up.

'Don't worry,' he said. 'This envelope is buff – for your
bit of stuff.'*

He has such a way with words.

I wish he had had more of a way with envelopes.

'This is the buff – for the old bit of rough,' he reminded
himself as he gave Edith the wrong one.

'This one is white – for the bit of all right,' he said as
he gave Yvette the other one.

* *I have questioned my mother closely about this reference, which seems
  to me to hold the key to so much of what went on undercover. 'René,'
  she has always responded, 'the war was very complicated, and there
  are some things that we simply cannot bring out into the open, even
  now.'*

To make matters worse, Edith then left Yvette's note by the till and Mimi found it. She, in turn, thought I had written to her.

'Aah,' she gasped in that small but perfectly formed way of hers. 'I would follow that man to the ends of the earth.'

Colonel Von Strohm and Lieutenant Gruber felt the same. They boarded the Geneva Express dressed as guards. Helga boarded it dressed as a beautiful spy.

'I have reserved one first-class sleeper to Geneva, please,' she said to the ticket-seller.

'Name?' he asked.

'Madame X.'

The Colonel's plan was for Madame X to insinuate herself into the compartment of the art expert, Yup Von Hoop De Hoop, drug his wine, and get the keys to the safe in the guard's van. Lieutenant Gruber would then substitute the forgeries for the original paintings.

The plan might have worked, had Herr Flick and Von Smallhausen not also been aboard the train.

'Members of the public are not allowed in here,' a steward told them as they barged into the buffet car.

'We are members of the Gestapo,' said Herr Flick. 'Take off your white monkey jackets and leave the train.'

'But it is moving,' the steward protested.

'Then you had better start running before you touch the ground.'

15 NOVEMBER

It is way past midnight. I have woken in a cold sweat. There are some things that a man sees and does in wartime that are not easily forgotten. I will try and tell you about them tomorrow.

16 NOVEMBER

No I won't.

17 NOVEMBER

Oh, very well.
   I, meanwhile, was just arriving in my compartment.
Our bunk, 4B, the upper one, was curtained off.
   The curtain moved a little as I undressed.
   'Is that you?' I whispered.
   'Yes, my love,' came the reply.
   There was a wonderful smell of perfume.

'I have poured a whole bottle over myself,' said the woman of my dreams. 'I feel like a girl.'

'You are a girl,' I cooed.

'Can you get up without a ladder?' she asked me.

As if she didn't know. I took off the rest of my clothes. Well, I said to myself, this is the first night of the rest of my life. I pulled aside the curtain.

The look of joy on Edith's face still haunts me.

'René, I cannot believe this is happening,' she said.

Neither could I.

The train was travelling at seventy miles an hour so I decided I could not throw myself off. It was a decision I came to regret.

18 NOVEMBER

I discovered afterwards that Mimi, Yvette and Leclerc had also somehow managed to join the party. The moral is: one should never put anything in writing.*

I got rid of Mimi by saying that the best thing for her was a quick jump. After a lot of explaining, she finally understood that I meant from the train into the river alongside.

Leclerc told me only once that Michelle was going to drop two exploding Christmas puddings down the funnel of the engine as we went under the bridge at Abbeville. I was just wondering what else could go wrong when the lights went out and there was an earth-shattering bang. It was that kind of evening.

Edith and I made it home across the fields. Luckily she

---

* Except, presumably, if you take the precaution of concealing the result inside an exploding Christmas pudding.

didn't find out that our serving girls had also been on the train.

Poor Yvette came all the way on a borrowed pair of roller skates.

Monsieur Leclerc came most of the way with her, except that just outside Nouvion he broke the balls of his bearings.

Mimi, too, made it back – soaked to the skin and covered in greed weed. I put my arms around her shoulders to warm her up.

'Mimi,' I said, 'your bosom is wriggling with delight.'

'It is a trout,' she said, reaching into her bra and pulling out a fish.

25 NOVEMBER

It has crossed my mind that I rather thought I would be in Switzerland when the General discovered that the gold had gone. Now I am in Nouvion. We could all be shot. I must go and put it back.

'Do not wirry,' Crabtree said to me. 'I have squoozed into the lock hard-sitting glue. If he cannot open the soof he will not knee that it is gin.'

I said that I was considering leaving by the next train.

'There are no troons,' he said. 'The one that was derooled by the Christmas pidding is still blicking the loon.'

This is not my day.

26 NOVEMBER

Nor this.

But at least Edith has had a brilliant idea. We have in the cellar exploding Christmas puddings. Her plan is to squash one into the lock, light the fuse and stand well back.

29 NOVEMBER

The Colonel and Lieutenant Gruber have recovered the original paintings of the Fallen Madonna with the Big Boobies by Van Clomp and the Cracked Vase with the Big Daisies by Van Gogh and have secreted them inside a four-foot tall statue in the Colonel's office of a blackamoor with a screwable head.

Helga also reports that the forgeries have been recovered by Herr Flick who put in their place two other forgeries.

Life, it seems, is returning to normal – except that this time I seem to have been cut out of the action.

30 NOVEMBER

General Von Klinkerhoffen paid a visit to the Colonel's office this morning. He wanted Lieutenant Gruber to take his little tank to the police station, pick up the safe which contained some not very important papers, and transfer it to the château where the unimportant papers will be safe.

'Will that be all?' the Colonel asked.

'No, this statue, I rather like it. It would look nice in my château.'

'But General,' the Colonel protested, 'it is such a cheap and ugly thing.'

'Are you questioning my taste? I will take it. Guard – put that statue in my car.'

That'll teach them.

1 DECEMBER

There has been another big bang and again it wasn't exactly the kind I enjoyed.

We went to the police station as planned, with an exploding Christmas pudding.

'I will witch out of the window,' said Crabtree. 'If anyone comes this woo I will give you two wonks.'

Edith pushed half the pudding into the lock and lit the fuse. We ran for cover, not noticing that Crabtree was wonking in the corner. Gruber had arrived. Bertorelli and his men were heading into the police station to help lift the safe into his little tank.

'I think the fuse has gone out,' said Edith. 'It has stopped fizzing.'

Just to be on the safe side, we ran like the clappers out of the back door.

Straight into Lieutenant Gruber.

'Oh, René, I keep meeting you in the most unexpected places,' he said.

'I was just reporting a missing hen,' I said.

The Lieutenant offered me a spin in his little tank on the way back to the Colonel's.

'Well, that is a very kind thought, Lieutenant, but this time I will give it a miss if it is all the same to you.'

Bertorelli stepped forward.

'Me, I have never been-a in-a the German tank. I travel-a with you.'

I could not stand idly by.

'Lieutenant,' I said, 'perhaps the Captain would like to drive the tank while you come and have a drink with me.'

'Oh, an invitation I cannot refuse.'

'You watch-a your Capitano go off in-a cloud of smoke, eh?' Bertorelli called to his men from the turret.

'Don't give it too much throttle,' Gruber cautioned him, 'otherwise you will get a little backfire.'

The tank exploded.

Bertorelli emerged from the wreckage in blackened underwear.

'I give him too much-a throttle,' he said.

2 DECEMBER

All's well that ends well. Captain Bertorelli lost his uniform, the feathers from his hat, and his no-claims bonus, but General Von Klinkerhoffen salvaged his gold from the wreck – and fortunately he did not get his hands on the four bars I stole earlier. With great cunning Yvette and I have melted them down in the kitchen and moulded them into a new weight for the cuckoo clock. Everyone admires its shape and length, particularly Lieutenant Gruber.

For the Lieutenant of course the loss of his little tank was a terrible wrench. He'd had so many happy moments in it. But fortunately the General was so pleased to recover his gold that he has ordered him a new model. Gruber is beside himself. When it arrives from the showroom it will be the only tank in the Corps with a G registration.

3 DECEMBER

Sadly, there are two slightly sour postscripts to the affair. The first is that the General now knows that four of his gold bars are missing. The second is that the finger of suspicion apparently points at me.

The Colonel, fortunately, has decided to do a deal. He will not enquire too closely into the whereabouts of the gold if I agree to help him with a little problem that he has.

'Colonel, it is as good as done.'

'The General has commandeered a statue in which we had secreted the original painting of the Fallen Madonna with the Big Boobies by Van Clomp and the Cracked Vase with the Big Daisies by Van Gogh. The General has taken the statue to his château. You are going to recover the paintings for us.'

'But I am just a humble café-owner,' I backtracked rapidly on my hasty promise. 'I do not get invited to the château. And I am a rotten burglar.'

It went without saying that Helga had a plan. The General is giving a dance which will be attended by the Generals who are planning the invasion of England. He has booked for this occasion the Palm Court Quartet from the Hotel Excelsior in Deauville. They will not arrive. The Colonel's men will stop them at a checkpoint. Their place will be taken by a scratch crew from the Café René.

'But Colonel, we are not musicians.'

'Helga has thought of this.'

In the château there is, apparently, a most up-to-date electric amplifying system. The Colonel has records of the quartet which Helga will play upon a concealed turntable.

Dear Mutti,
    Herr Flick is being mean to me about my application for promotion. He yelled for me to go into his quarters this morning. In his hands he held my form.
    "You are of course aware that you are only a provisional member of the Gestapo?"
    "Yes Herr Flick."
    "You have applied here for promotion to Grade 3 Officer, are you prepared to take the test?"
I have been in training, Mutti. It is my dearest wish to move up the ladder.
    Herr Flick sat me down in the chair opposite him

and switched on the spotlight so that it shone in my face.

'The subject that you have chosen is Hitler. You have 30 seconds to answer five questions, starting now.'

'One. What was Herr Hitler's occupation before he became Führer?'

'Painter.'

'Correct. What is regarded as his best work?'

'The iron railings outside 37 Winklestrasser.'

'Correct. What was the name of the barber who created his silly hairstyle?'

'Pass.'

'Correct. Herr Ludwig Pass. You have scored ten points. Stand up. You will now perform the physical tests. Are you ready?'

'Yes, Herr Flick.'

I opened my coat. I was wearing PT shorts and a singlet.

'You have failed,' he said. 'Now pay attention. It is my belief that the purpose of the Officer's Dance at the Château is to further the plot to blow up Hitler.'

'We will infiltrate ourselves into this shindig. We will obtain the names of those present and their photographs. Here is the camera that you will conceal upon your person.'

It was quite a big one, Mutti, I asked him where he suggested I hide it.

'It is up to you, Von Smallhausen,' he said with characteristic superiority and disregard for my feelings. 'If you are unsuccessful you will also fail your "concealing a camera" test.'

Oh Mutti, what can a man do.

urs up to his neck in it,

Bobby Cedric Von Smallhausen

We from the café will only appear to play. We will set up our orchestra near the statue, and while we are only appearing to play we will unscrew the head, take out the paintings and replace the head.

'But how can I do this with everyone looking on?' I asked.

'That, René,' said the Colonel, 'is your problem.'

'Get your friends in the Resistance who you do not know to help you,' quipped Helga.

I think they have entirely the wrong idea about me. All I want to do is run my café and lead a nice quiet life until the war is over.*

12 DECEMBER

Michelle says the Germans have a new machine for encoding messages. It is called Enema.

It is incredible the lengths the Germans will go to in order to pass messages.

13 DECEMBER

Correction, it is Enigma. London want us to nick it from the Parson's Nose. That is secret radio code for the headquarters of the General.

Michelle has a plan. And if I had ten francs for every time I have written that, I would be a wealthier man than even Monsieur Alfonse.

The Enigma machine is in the room next to the salon where we of the Excelsior Quartet will be knocking them dead in the aisles tomorrow night. Mimi is to be concealed in the case of the double bass. I will place it near the door.

---

* And, of course, do his bit for France. As usual René is selling himself short.

When the revelry is at its height Mimi will climb out of the case, slip into the room, grab the machine and throw it out of the window where members of the Resistance will be waiting below to catch it in a blanket. She's as bright as a button, that girl. She thinks of everything. She doesn't need me around as leader any more.

'Michelle,' I asked modestly, 'could you not possibly find me a desk job in the Resistance?'

'René, the girls could not survive without your movements underground.'

I have to say that I've had no complaints about my movements above ground either.

Herr Flick inspects Helga's accessories before escorting her to the Gestapo dinner/dance.

14 DECEMBER

Plans, it seems, are all the rage. Edith's is that when we set up our instruments we conceal somebody in the piano and place it near the statue.

'Edith,' I reasoned, 'we are a quartet. You will play the violin, I will play the piano, Monsieur Leclerc will play the cello, Mimi is in the case – who is going to play the bass and who is going to hide in the piano?'

'I could hide in the piano,' said Yvette.

'But who will hold open the lid while you reach out to unscrew the head of the statue?' Mimi asked.

'And that will still leave somebody to play the bass,' I said. 'Edith, your plan will not work because you are still short of two people.'

It was at that moment that there was a knock at the door and in came Monsieur Alfonse, the old undertaker with the dicky ticker and the tricky truss, and the British agent Crabtree, the idiot who thinks he can speak our language.

16 DECEMBER

I wish I could report that all had gone according to plan.

The dance was indeed a glittering occasion. All the top brass were there. So, at the Itie table, were all the top feathers. Herr Flick and Von Smallhausen had successfully infiltrated the gathering dressed as maids, carrying trays of snacks. Von Smallhausen had a very pronounced bosom.

From where I was sitting at the piano, I could see and hear everything.

'Are your sausages prepared?' Herr Flick asked his fellow maid.

'The sticks are firmly thrust into them.'

'Have you tested your camera?'

'Not yet.'

'Then do so.'

I watched in amazement as Von Smallhausen squeezed one of his bosoms. A lace pocket in the other bosom flew open, revealing a lens. It shut again very quickly.

'Good,' said Herr Flick. 'You have ten feet of film nestling in your left booby. Make the most of it.'

They circulated with their sausages and the Excelsior Quartet struck up. Everything went well to start with. Then the idiot Crabtree got carried away and launched into his party piece, a slightly less than perfect impersonation of Maurice Chevalier.

19 DECEMBER

I am very close to a complete nervous breakdown.

For the last few days I have been harbouring once again the original canvases of the Fallen Madonna with the Big Boobies and the Cracked Vase with the Big Daisies – as well as the secret coding apparatus called Enigma. The Resistance had been trying to get it to England by placing it in a wine barrel and floating it into the town drain to be picked up by a two-man midget submarine.

To do this the entire population of Nouvion were supposed to flush their toilets at one and the same time. Needless to say, there was a cock-up. The barrel that they put into the drain contained not a coding machine but some underwear belonging to Yvette which even as I write is probably in the hands of the head of MI5 who is probably trying to decode it.

He will find nothing of interest, except that Yvette is very well built.*

20 DECEMBER

We are no longer trying to send the Enigma machine to the experts in London.

Instead, the experts are going to come here to examine it. They will be dropped by parachute and disguised as policemen. My heart sinks.

When they arrive at the café these agents will make themselves known by means of a secret sign. They will brandish their truncheons in a special way as if they were, well, truncheons being brandished in a special way. Anyway, it is not a gesture that will go unnoticed.

'You will then give us a signal and we will deliver the machine,' Michelle said.

'What will be the nature of this signal?' asked Edith.

'You will place a red cycle lamp in the window of the bedroom of your mother.'

'A red lamp! What will the neighbours think?'

---

*   And that, as René implies, is no secret.

'You can say she is being repaired by a road gang,' I suggested.

When the signal has been sent, the Engima machine will be delivered by – who else? – another of their agents disguised as a Spanish accordion-player.

21 DECEMBER

The Enigma machine has now been missing for three days and, from what I can gather, the wires to Berlin have been smoking. Hitler is electrified with fury at General Von Klinkerhoffen. He has delivered an ultimatum. If the machine is not recovered within twenty-four hours the General is to be sent to the Russian Front.

The General has decided that he prefers the Nouvion climate, and has therefore delivered the Colonel an ultimatum of his own. Either the machine is recovered before Christmas Day or I, as the most prominent and likeable figure in the town, am to be marched to the square and shot. I wonder if there is time to commission a quick opinion poll to show that when it comes to prominence and popularity, you can't beat a good piano player like Roger Leclerc?

23 DECEMBER

One of my Christmas wishes came true this afternoon. Edith was arrested by the Gestapo and taken off for interrogation. Unfortunately, so were Yvette and Mimi.

I'll spend the next twenty-four hours or so planning my heroic rescue. There's no way I'll find replacement staff at this short notice.

Helga begins to wonder whether she has arrived at the wrong party.

24 DECEMBER

Lieutenant Gruber arrived early this evening dressed in Helga's uniform. At first I assumed it was his way of getting into the festive mood. But no, he came to warn me that Colonel Von Strohm had reacted badly to the General's ultimatum.

'There have been one or two very serious developments, René,' he said.

'So I see,' I replied.

'The Colonel confiscated my uniform in case I should

tip you the wink. I pinched this while Helga was having a bath.'

The Colonel had taken the view that he must obey orders and start peasant shooting unless the Enigma machine is returned. He's chalked up six of our names for starters; at eight o'clock tomorrow morning his men will arrest a café-owner, his wife, his two waitresses, and the piano-player.

Lieutenant Gruber and that little smile of his that René finds so unsettling.

'Chuck in the undertaker,' the Colonel had ordered Helga.

'Who's going to bury them?' she asked.

'Shoot him last.'

As the Lieutenant spoke I gazed up at the Christmas tree that Yvette and I had so lovingly decorated before she was taken away. I had a sudden vision of myself being hung up by the balls.

'This looks like being a very unhappy Christmas,' I said.

The Lieutenant grabbed a menu and covered his face. Helga had finished her bath. She was now advancing on the bar wearing a greatcoat and tin helmet.

'Helga,' I greeted her, 'what a pretty helmet. Are you on manoeuvres?'

The reply came through clenched lips. 'No. I am on tranquillisers. My uniform has been stolen. Look.'

As she opened her coat I could see immediately that she was right.

'I suspect Lieutenant Gruber took it in order to warn you of your impending fate.'

'I am sure it could not have been Lieutenant Gruber,' I said. 'He would have taken the underwear as well.'

Fortunately, Yvette and Mimi returned to the café just as things were hotting up. Edith was with them. Something rather extraordinary had happened. Herr Flick had administered to them a truth drug in a tea-bag, a new German invention by Baron Von Tetley. I recognised it as having been distilled from the sweat glands of the Patagonian fruit-bat. Unluckily for the Gestapo it had been a faulty batch. The three were released after lying about their age and emitting a series of high-pitched squeaks.

Mimi had been affected the worst. She went instantly to the larder and hung upside down by the hams.

I looked at my watch. It was almost time to don my fancy dress for the Christmas Eve celebrations. I was coming as Toulouse Lautrec. I wondered how long it would take to get to the Swiss border on my knees. Unless the Enigma machine was returned, I had less than twelve hours before the party was over.

At that moment, things really started to go with a swing. The two British agents arrived dressed as policemen, truncheons at the ready. That idiot Crabtree

Herr Flick tells Edith that there are some things he definitely does not want her to reveal.

joined them and there was much excitement. Apparently they had been at longwodge school together.

By the time Monsieur Alfonse and that old fool Leclerc turned up, dressed as Spanish accordion-players, the

truncheons were going full blast. The Enigma machine was concealed in one of the accordions.

'We will arrost the moosicians and take them into the back rim where we will disciver its secrets,' Crabtree told Michelle, who had appeared like a phantom out of the evening.

'You will disciver them only once,' I said. 'The General, the Colonel and the Itie Captain are coming across the square.'

Michelle and the Polooce made a bee-line for the back room with the machine. Captain Bertorelli made a bee-line for Lieutenant Gruber.

'You,' he said manfully, 'how-a you like the good time with the big-a de hero?'

'You must forgive me,' Gruber replied, 'but I am not very keen on moustaches.'

It was the first I had heard of it.

I was heading to the door for a breath of fresh air as General Von Klinkerhoffen decided enough was enough.

He placed a hand on my shoulder and ordered the Colonel to prepare for my immediate execution.

Herr Flick and Von Smallhausen entered with guns. For a moment I wasn't sure whether this party was going to be a total success.

The Crabtree appeared from the parlour dressed as Father Christmas.

'Gentlemen, I have good nose,' he said. And for once he was root. 'The Resoostance, who have no idea of Roné's exoostance, have just throon the Enigma machine through the window of the back rim.'

There was a crash of breaking glass.

'That must be it now,' I said. I thought seriously about giving my guests a drink on the house.

'The matter is now closed,' the General said. 'Now I must call my tailor to cancel my winter uniform.'

'Again I am thwarted,' Herr Flick grimaced.

'So am I,' Von Smallhausen squeaked.

Herr Flick had the last word. 'Your thwart is smaller.'

31 DECEMBER

Needless to say, my Christmas was as active as ever. My stocking was full of little goodies and, despite rationing, so was Yvette's.

Lieutenant Gruber's were too, by all accounts, until Helga insisted that he return them to her in time for Herr Flick's traditional Yuletide interrogation. He holds it in his dungeon immediately after Hitler's Christmas speech.

The Colonel celebrated, as always, with the flying helmet, the egg whisk and some wet mistletoe. From time to time he nipped down to the cellar to make sure that his knockwursts were in safe hands.

That idiot Leclerc only emerged once from the bedroom of my wife's mother. He was disguised very convincingly as the ghost of Christmas Past.

I found the sight of Mimi hanging from my bedstead a little alarming, especially after dark, but I got used to it. After a while she began to remind me of the early days of my marriage to Edith.

The British airmen are also still hanging around, of course. They must be the only two turkeys to have made it past Christmas.